THE NEUTRON STORY

THE COVER: A conception of the possible paths of a proton (blue, top) and a neutron (red, below) as they shoot into a group of atoms (see page 22).

DONALD J. HUGHES, author of *The Neutron Story,* is one of the gifted young physicists who worked on the atom bomb project in World War II and thus helped to usher in the nuclear age.

At the age of forty-three Dr. Hughes is a senior physicist at the Brookhaven National Laboratory, Upton, Long Island, where he directs a group doing pile neutron research. He has been a Fulbright professor at Oxford and Cambridge universities in England, has lectured at fifteen research institutes in Poland and the Soviet Union, and has been appointed a United States representative to the second International Conference on Peaceful Uses of Atomic Energy. *The Neutron Story* is his sixth book. The Russians translated three of the others and found one so impressive that they ordered a first printing of 20,000 copies, by American standards an incredible number for a highly technical work.

Dr. Hughes was born on April 2, 1915, in Chicago, son of a telephone company construction superintendent. His original ambition was to become a telephone engineer, but he won a competitive physics examination for a scholarship at the University of Chicago and found his true calling. After receiving his Ph.D. at twenty-five he remained at the university to teach. He took his doctor's degree in the field of cosmic rays and was a member of a 1941 cosmic ray expedition to South America.

In 1942 the Navy called him to Washington to direct a section on underwater research at the Naval Ordnance Laboratory. Early in 1943 he joined the Manhattan Project at the University of Chicago when the first atomic pile was going into operation. He spent 1944 at Hanford, Washington, when the project started operating the large chain-reacting piles for production of plutonium. In 1945 the Atomic Energy Commission made him director of the Nuclear Physics Division of the Argonne National Laboratory in Chicago. He went to Brookhaven in 1949.

At Argonne, Dr. Hughes collaborated with Dr. Wilber D. B. Spatz and Dr. Norman Goldstein in developing a method to measure fast neutron cross sections. It became the basis of Dr. George Gamow's theory of the origin of the elements and was applied to the design of fast neutron breeder reactors, like the one in operation at Arco, Idaho. His Brookhaven group has accomplished significant work with neutron "mirrors," developed the "fast chopper" of great value in nuclear investigations, and has originated techniques of working with "cold" neutrons.

His previous books are *Pile Neutron Research* (1953); *Neutron Optics* (1954); *Neutron Cross Sections* (1957); *On Nuclear Energy* (1957), and a compilation *Neutron Cross Sections,* which the Government Printing Office published for the second Geneva conference. He also has contributed articles to general magazines as well as scientific journals.

Away from the laboratory, Dr. Hughes fits the public picture of a genial (and successful) young corporation lawyer or physician better than he does the popular image of a scientist. With his young wife, Valerie, and their baby daughter, he lives at Bellport, Long Island, a pleasant community overlooking the Great South Bay. He has a passion for sailboating, loves music and travel. How he finds time for all his activities astounds his friends.

4

THE NEUTRON STORY

by Donald J. Hughes

Published by
Doubleday Anchor Books
Doubleday & Company, Inc.
Garden City, New York
1959

Available to secondary
school students and teachers through
Wesleyan University Press Incorporated
Columbus 16, Ohio

COVER DESIGN BY GEORGE GIUSTI
ILLUSTRATIONS BY PERCY H. LUND

This book is dedicated to Enrico Fermi

THE SCIENCE STUDY SERIES

The Science Study Series offers to students and to the general public the writing of distinguished authors on the most stirring and fundamental topics of physics, from the smallest known particles to the whole universe. Some of the books tell of the role of physics in the world of man, his technology and his civilization. Others are biographical in nature, telling the fascinating stories of the great discoverers and their discoveries. All the authors have been selected both for expertness in the fields they discuss and for ability to communicate their special knowledge and their own views in an interesting way. The primary purpose of these books is to provide an authoritative survey of physics within the grasp of the young student or the layman. Many of the books, it is hoped, will encourage the reader to make his own investigations of natural phenomena.

These books are published as a part of a fresh approach to the teaching and study of physics. At the Massachusetts Institute of Technology during 1956 a group of physicists, high school teachers, journalists, apparatus designers, film producers, and other specialists organized the Physical Science Study Committee, now operating as a part of Educational Services Incorporated, Watertown, Massachusetts. They pooled their knowledge and experience toward the design and creation of aids to the learning of physics. Initially their effort was supported by the National Science Foundation, which has continued to aid the program. The Ford Foundation, the Fund for the Advancement of Education, and the Alfred P. Sloan Foundation have also given support. The Committee is creating a textbook, an extensive film series, a laboratory guide, especially designed apparatus, and a teacher's source book for a new integrated secondary school physics program which is undergoing continuous evaluation with secondary school teachers.

The Series is guided by the Board of Editors of the Physical Science Study Committee, consisting of Paul F. Brandwein, the Conservation Foundation and Harcourt, Brace and Company; John H. Durston, Educational Services Incorporated; Laura Fermi, author; Francis L. Friedman, Massachusetts Institute of Technology; Samuel A. Goudsmit, Brookhaven National Laboratory; Bruce F. Kingsbury, Educational Services Incorporated; Philippe LeCorbeiller, Harvard University; Gerard Piel, *Scientific American;* and Herbert S. Zim, Simon and Schuster, Inc.

PREFACE

I had the extremely good fortune to learn about neutrons directly from Enrico Fermi, starting with the first nuclear chain reaction in 1942 and continuing for many years thereafter until his death in 1954. Thus, when asked by Mrs. Fermi, who was then on the P.S.S.C. staff, to write this brief story of the neutron, I was happy to take on the task. It promised to give me an opportunity to pass on to many individuals the zest for penetrating the nature of matter so unfailingly displayed by Fermi. And the writing has been a most pleasant experience; in putting into words the significance of the neutron's behavior, I have had constantly in mind the stimulation of many discussions with Fermi in which these concepts became clarified to me.

As an integral part of the high school physics teaching program, this book deals with a special topic not included in the normal course work. Because the neutron illustrates fundamental physical laws so well, gives so much information about atomic structure, and in addition has wide practical applications, it is a fitting subject for a monograph of the series. In spite of its place in the teaching program, however, I have written the book in such a way that its understanding does not depend on the classroom material. Actually I have kept three rather distinct groups of readers in mind. There are first of all the young students who will go ahead to do pioneering research on their own; secondly, those who are studying science in high school but will proceed to many non-scientific fields; and finally the general readers, pursuing no course work, who are interested in the meaning of modern science.

In spite of the great differences that might be expected among these three groups, it was happily not difficult to write one book for all. I felt it unnecessary to include extensive mathematics or technical language to explain the nature and accomplishments of the neutron. Nor did the inherent attraction of the subatomic world require sensational treatment for its appreciation. *The Neutron Story,* I feel, is scientific fact whose meaning and beauty can be transmitted without higher mathematics or headlines. It is my conviction that in this you will agree—the story has elements of mystery, profundity, and beauty, whose significance can be conveyed to those without technical training who are willing to put their minds to it.

The preparation of this book, small as it is, has involved the co-operation of many people. Among these, I would particularly like to thank Mrs. Laura Fermi, who provided me with the opportunity to tell the neutron story, and to Dr. S. A. Goudsmit, who has helped generously at every stage. Mrs. Jeanne Stough aided greatly the preparation of the manuscript, while George R. Cox and Dr. Robert C. Garth helped with the illustrations. In the conversion of the manuscript to an actual book, I am especially grateful to John H. Durston and Bruce F. Kingsbury, of the Physical Science Study Committee, and Mrs. Lee Wertheim.

DONALD J. HUGHES

CONTENTS

CONTENTS

THE NEUTRON STORY

CHAPTER 1

The Versatile Neutron

We are accustomed to hearing tales of wonder and
mystery—usually of places far off or times long ago.
Yet there are other realms of wonder and mystery—
the inner nature of familiar objects, if we can but see
them truly. As witnessed with our five senses, these objects
may seem prosaic indeed. But with the marvelous
sixth sense of sensitive instruments, it is as if a new
world within matter is experienced, wonderful almost
beyond comprehension. And this world of the very
small has a further fascination—unlike the fairy tale,
it is true. It is a strange world, this realm of subatomic
entities, but a very real one. Much of it remains un-
explored, perhaps always will, though the pace of exploration hastens every day. As our knowledge of it
has continued to grow, sometimes slowly and labo-
riously, sometimes by leaps, we have discovered new
instruments to assist in our investigations. It is one of
those tools that is the subject of this book, and it is
in keeping with the nature of the world of the very
small that it should be a tiny, uncharged bit of matter.

* * *

It may seem strange to devote an entire book to a single particle, and a small one at that. The purpose of our story is simple: to describe the nature and exploits of the *neutron*. True, the story deals with complex things; before we are through, we shall at least have speculated on some of the universe's most awesome mysteries and have studied man's most stupendous scientific achievement. But before getting into our story, let us consider why, in so spectacular a setting, the minute neutron should merit so much attention.

Although chemists, physicists, and mathematicians had been learning about the atomic structure of matter for generations, a short thirty years ago the neutron had no place in their thinking, for it was unknown. But so important is this particle in today's physics that a whole field of research—neutron physics—is based on its properties. And this new branch of science, young as it is, touches on so many phases of pure research, and has so many important practical applications, that it actually is much more than a single field of endeavor. We need think only of the large-scale production of electrical power from atomic energy or the propulsion of giant, swift submarines to realize the spectacular usefulness of the neutron. In addition to these dramatic applications, the neutron performs important functions in the realm of "pure" or basic science, in which practical results are not the objective. The neutron's accomplishments here are not nearly as impressive to the eye as atomic power but probably will be of greater ultimate benefit to mankind.

How can it be that within thirty years this bit of matter has proved to be so versatile? Another and very similar particle, the *proton,* although known much longer, has produced nothing comparable to the feats of the neutron. There is no field of research called "proton physics" in spite of the fact that the fundamental properties of the proton have been familiar for a long time.

In structure the proton and the neutron are much alike. They differ primarily in that the proton bears a positive electrical charge, while the neutron, as its name implies, is electrically neutral. Yet this apparently rather trivial difference—the lack of an electrical charge—is the underlying source of the astonishing diversity of neutron physics. In our story we shall learn some of the fascinating details of the many ways in which neutrons serve as sensitive tools in the most fundamental research and have important practical applications as well. But first we should understand why the lack of an electrical charge is the basis of the neutron's potency.

The neutrality is so important because practically all other components of matter are electrically charged. Protons are positive, most electrons negative; atoms, although neutral as a whole, are made up of positive nuclei surrounded by electrons. As we know, electrical charges exert strong forces on one another, forces of attraction if the charges are unlike and forces of repulsion if they are the same. To make our point clear, let us imagine that we are going to investigate or to change the inner structure, the atoms, of a piece of matter by bombarding it with fast atomic particles as probes. We would find great difficulty should we choose charged particles—protons, say—for our atomic bullets. For example, a proton shot into a sample of material would be brought to rest rapidly by the electrical forces between its charge and the negatively charged electrons of the material's atoms. Could we observe such tiny entities as atoms and their component electrons, a small section of our sample would appear as we have sketched in Figure 1. Because of the electrical interaction that quickly reduces the energy of the proton, it is necessary to have high

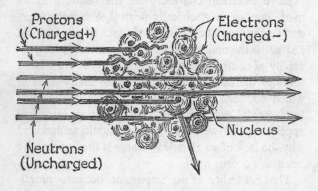

Fig. 1. Penetrating power of the neutron is vastly greater than the proton's. The attractive force of the atoms' negatively charged electrons quickly stops the positively charged protons. Except for rare collisions with nuclei, the uncharged neutrons penetrate matter unhindered. This illustration (like the others in this book) is a symbolic representation of what we know of the constituents of matter, not a true picture. We cannot picture subatomic particles accurately because they have properties beyond our everyday experience. Hence, we must adopt a model or symbol, but it can give only an idea of the properties scientists have deduced from indirect evidence and theoretical calculations.

initial speed in order to use protons to investigate matter at all.

But neutrons, having no electrical charge, pass easily into the material, unimpeded by the electric charges of its electrons. As we see in Figure 1, neutrons travel along straight paths with complete disregard of the atoms, unless they happen to collide head-on with the atom's nucleus. The neutron would not require high speed to penetrate the material, and in fact could do it when moving very slowly. As we shall learn later, the properties of the neutron, as of all particles, vary tremendously with its speed. Thus, in order to accomplish specific jobs with neutrons, whether in research or application, it is important to be able to use neutrons of the best speed for each task. Because neutrons of any desired speed can enter freely into material, the entire range of speed is available and the best speed for the purpose can be chosen. Our entire story, in fact, will illustrate how the lack of charge is the fundamental property that has made neutrons, in the short time they have been known to man, of extreme value in almost all fields of pure and applied science.

Perhaps it would help at this point to outline these accomplishments of the neutron in its "lifetime" of less than thirty years, and later we shall consider the most striking ones intensively. Since the circumstances of its "birth"—that is, its discovery—bear all the characteristics of a first-rate mystery, we shall devote our next chapter to that fascinating story and confine ourselves here to pointing out that the neutron, born as recently as 1932, is now in the full vigor of young manhood.

Indeed, it did not wait many years to show its

prowess, for in 1939, at the age of seven, the neutron became the means for demonstrating the fission of uranium. This is the process that showed for the first time that appreciable amounts of matter might actually be destroyed, and that in its place energy would appear. The amount of energy, long before predicted by Einstein's equation $E = mc^2$, was extremely large, and the discovery marked the advent of an important new fuel—mass itself. And in 1942, at the tender age of ten, the neutron participated in the successful release of energy from mass on a practical scale in the controlled chain reaction.

Just three years later this chain reaction, involving neutrons and uranium, was adapted to produce an atomic bomb. Soon afterward World War II ended. Then it was time for the neutron to show that it had great potentialities in non-military fields as well. The neutron's functions in fields beneficial to man advanced rapidly—so rapidly, in fact, that within a few years the peacetime uses of atomic energy became a matter of international organization. The neutron was just twenty-one years old when President Eisenhower proposed, in a speech before the United Nations General Assembly in December 1953, that an international agency to speed the beneficial use of atomic energy be established. Two years later the first worldwide Atoms for Peace Conference was held in Geneva, and the great wealth of technical material presented at this conference on nuclear power was definite proof of the stature of the neutron, then twenty-three years old, in the field of practical accomplishments. The twenty-sixth year of the neutron's life was marked by the second Geneva Conference, more than twice the size of the first. And the International

Atomic Energy Agency became an established body, with headquarters in Vienna and over eighty member nations.

Yet important as these practical matters are—the production of electrical power, motive power for ships, and radioisotopes for medical and industrial uses—it is the function of the neutron in pure research that we shall consider. These uses are much more difficult to describe, and much more subtle, than such obvious things as atomic submarines. But their story is every bit as fascinating. In basic research we are dealing with the laws that are fundamental to *all* matter and its manifestations, whether in the small world of the atom or on the astronomical scale of the galaxies. The neutron, being a basic building block of all matter, is of particular importance in the discovery and understanding of these fundamental laws. Even the properties of the neutron itself, separate from other objects, provide much information on the innermost structure of matter. Still more fruitful, however, are its interactions with other particles and with bulk matter; they reveal in many sensitive ways the most basic relationships among the ultimate particles underlying the structure of all things. So, with the immense importance of this particle in mind, let us turn first to the puzzle whose solution led to the discovery of the neutron, then to the fascinating properties of the neutron itself and its varied behavior with respect to all forms of matter.

CHAPTER 2

Puzzles and Solutions

The first demonstration of the neutron's importance in modern physics took place immediately after its discovery: It was instrumental in solving the problem of the nature of the nucleus, which itself had been known for only eighteen years. Before we recount the story of the neutron's discovery and its place in nuclear structure, however, we must first review some of the simple facts about the atom, concentrating on its central core, the nucleus. Having done so, we then can appreciate much better the fundamental significance of the neutron and at the same time witness the dramatic way in which the important advances in science sometimes are made. But we shall not lose sight of the fact that the discovery of the neutron, sudden and stirring as it was, rested firmly on a large number of previous careful investigations; combined, they made the final break-through possible.

The Atom and the Nucleus

During the eighteenth and nineteenth centuries, chemists slowly had been accumulating evidence that

27

all matter was composed of very small particles called *atoms,* too tiny by far to be seen through even the most powerful microscopes. By observing how various materials reacted with each other, they had been able to make accurate determinations of the relative weights and sizes of these invisible particles and to learn something about the ways in which a few different kinds of atoms combine to form the great diversity of substances that make up our world. Thus, *elements,* such as hydrogen, oxygen, iron, copper, and so on, were known to be particularly simple substances, for each is composed of one particular kind of atom only; other materials, called *compounds*, contain more than one kind of atom, as we see in Figure 2. An atom of an element is essentially unchanged when it combines with others even though the properties

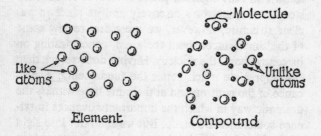

Like atoms

Molecule

Unlike atoms

Element

Compound

Fig. 2. Nature's diversity results from elements combining into compounds. Elements are made up of atoms of a single kind. Compounds consist of molecules which may contain many kinds of atoms. The relationship of atoms to elements and of molecules to compounds is illustrated in this diagram. There are only 92 naturally occurring elements, but they combine in countless ways to create the world familiar to our senses.

obvious to our senses change markedly. For example, oxygen atoms in the form of oxygen gas in the atmosphere are the same as those that, combined with hydrogen atoms, form water. Long before the internal structure of atoms was studied, chemists had learned much about the elements, the one containing the lightest atoms being the gas hydrogen, and the heaviest, the metal uranium.

A multitude of experiments has gradually revealed the make-up of atoms. Most of the atomic volume is occupied by the orbits of rapidly moving electrons, each carrying one unit of negative electric charge. The hydrogen atom contains only one electron, uranium has 92. As electrons are extremely light, practically all the atom's weight is concentrated in a small central speck of matter—the *nucleus*. Detailed information about the weight of atoms and the manner in which they interact with one another by means of the electrons in their outermost regions had been learned through chemical experiments. These results, however, gave practically no information concerning the nucleus. In chemical changes, such as burning, it is only the outermost layers of electrons that are affected; the nucleus, buried far within the electrons, is completely unaffected.

It is even possible to infer from chemical behavior the number of electrons in the atoms of each element. Actually the Russian chemist Mendeléev had arranged all elements in a definite chemical order, extending from hydrogen to uranium. Although Mendeléev was not thinking in terms of electrons, for the electron had not yet been discovered, his arrangement of the elements was according to the number of electrons, one for hydrogen to 92 for uranium. Later it was found possible to verify his chemical ordering by means of x-rays; in the x-ray interactions with an atom the number of electrons can be measured directly. Again the order of the elements was the same —one electron for hydrogen, two for helium, and so on, to 92 for uranium.

Since atoms normally have no electric charge, obviously each atom must in some way contain an amount of positive electricity to balance the negative charge of the electrons. In addition, associated with this positive charge there must be most of the weight of the atom, for the electrons are extremely light. But chemical experiments could not tell where the positive charge and mass were located within the atom.

In 1914 the British physicist Ernest Rutherford discovered that the mass and positive charge were concentrated in a spot at the center of the atom. His experiment, marking the advent of nuclear physics, was accomplished by shooting *alpha particles,* produced from radium, through thin sheets of metal. In the process the alpha particles usually would pass through the foil and be scattered only slightly. But on rare occasions they would be deflected widely or even bounce back and not pass through the foil at all. These wide deflections (see Figure 3) could be caused, Rutherford reasoned, in no other way than by a small, electrically charged particle within the atom. A diffuse distribution of charged matter could never scatter the alpha particles through large angles. If, however, the charge was located practically at a point, the alpha particle would be powerfully repelled electrically should it chance to head directly toward this point. And indeed the nucleus is essentially a point relative to the size of the atom itself, for it is some ten thousand times smaller, about 10^{-12} cm across, compared with 10^{-8} cm for the atom.

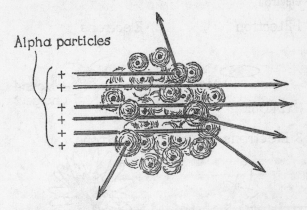

Alpha particles

Fig. 3. Rebounding alpha particle was the clue that led to Lord Rutherford's discovery of the nucleus, a great stride forward in the exploration of matter. He reasoned that the occasional large deflections of the particles could be explained only if the positive charge in the atom was concentrated at a tiny central spot—the nucleus.

The Puzzle of Nuclear Make-up

Even though the existence of the nucleus had been demonstrated, there remained a great puzzle about its actual constitution. The physicists' picture of the nucleus of the simplest atom, hydrogen, seemed to make sense, but there was a basic difficulty with all heavier atoms. The hydrogen atom is the lightest of all atoms and its mass is taken as unity—more accurately its *mass number* is unity. Its particularly simple nucleus is given a special name—the *proton*. The proton must

31

have a positive charge of one unit, for it was well known that the hydrogen atom contains only one electron.

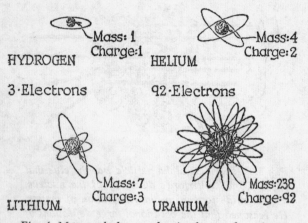

1·Electron   2·Electrons

HYDROGEN   Mass: 1   HELIUM   Mass: 4
          Charge: 1   Charge: 2

3·Electrons   92·Electrons

LITHIUM   Mass: 7   URANIUM   Mass: 238
         Charge: 3   Charge: 92

Fig. 4. Mass and charge—that is, the number of nuclear particles and the number of protons—are equal only in the hydrogen atom, which has a proton and an electron but no neutron. In all the other elements mass exceeds charge, greatly so in the heavy atoms. This illustration gives an idea of the variance in mass, charge, and number of electrons among the different elements.

The trouble began even with the next heavier atom, helium. It was known to contain two electrons, and, had its weight been twice that of hydrogen, things would have been simple, for its nucleus would obviously consist of two protons. But instead of being twice as heavy, the helium atom is *four* times as heavy as hydrogen. It has a mass number of four, yet a nuclear charge of only two units necessary to balance its two electrons.

For heavier atoms, as shown in Figure 4, things get no better. Like helium, their nuclei weigh about twice as much as they would if they consisted simply of protons, in number enough to balance the known number of electrons. For very heavy nuclei the situation gets even worse: The weight of uranium, for example, is about two and a half times as great as it would be if its nucleus consisted of protons only, in number equal to the number of electrons—that is, 92. There even were cases in which different atoms of the *same* element had different weights. Thus U^{235} and U^{238} are chemically alike, both atoms being uranium, containing 92 electrons, but their mass numbers differ by three units, 235 and 238. If nuclei consisted only of protons, no clue to the explanation of these *isotopes* was available.

Attempts were made to explain away these persistent discrepancies by assuming that electrons could be contained within the nucleus. The electrons, it was argued, would balance the positive charges of protons, making it possible to have extra weight without increasing the net positive charge on the nucleus. At first this possibility seemed to be a good one, for it would not only explain the excess weight but the existence of isotopes as well. But as the fundamental properties of protons and electrons became better known, it was realized that there was no possibility of electrons' residing inside the tiny nucleus. The reason is simply stated: Electrons are just too large to fit within the nucleus. But the full significance of this statement is much harder to comprehend. We shall see in the next chapter, dramatically demonstrated by neutrons, that every *particle* also has *wave* properties; that is, each particle acts like a wave, with a wave length determined by its speed, high speed corresponding to short wave length. For an electron to be "within" the nucleus it is necessary that its wave length be smaller than the size of the nucleus and its speed therefore very high. Unfortunately for this theory, the electron's energy would have to be extremely large, corresponding to a potential of fifty million volts. As energies of this magnitude are not available within the nucleus, this basic consideration rules out the hypothesis that electrons could be situated inside the nucleus.

The Neutron Is Discovered

Just as the theory of the nuclear constituents seemed to have reached an impasse, experiments were taking place that were apparently unrelated but were destined nevertheless to lead to the solution. These were experiments in which the *transmutation* of atoms of one element to those of another was accomplished by bombardment with alpha particles (helium nuclei). High-speed alpha particles were available because they are emitted spontaneously from radium and similar heavy nuclei. Rutherford accomplished the first such transmutation with alpha particles as projectiles in 1918, when he succeeded in changing a few atoms of nitrogen to oxygen. The nitrogen became fluorine by absorbing the alpha particle, and then by emitting a proton changed to oxygen.

In 1930 further studies of these transmutations were being carried on at various laboratories; here we are particularly interested in the work of Bothe and

Becker in Germany. In their experiments, when alpha particles were allowed to hit the metal beryllium, very penetrating radiations were produced, radiations that could easily pass through *several inches* of lead. Here indeed was an unexpected result, for the protons produced in the usual transmutation could be stopped by a very thin sheet of lead. The most penetrating radiations known at the time were *gamma rays,* the rays that are emitted by radium and are used, for example, to penetrate the human body to destroy cancer cells. But as the newly discovered radiations were more penetrating than the most powerful gamma rays known, it seemed highly unlikely that they also could be gamma rays.

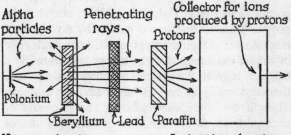

Fig. 5. Penetrating radiation was discovered by Bothe and Becker. Alpha particles bombarding beryllium create a radiation that easily passes through lead and ejects fast protons from a material containing hydrogen.

The mysterious radiations were detected in a gas-filled *ionization chamber,* shown in Figure 5, which records the amount of electricity, or *ionization,* removed from gas atoms by particles passing through

35

it. Blocks of lead placed in the path of the radiations, as shown, revealed their great penetrating power. A second and even more amazing discovery was then made. Thin sheets of materials containing hydrogen —for example, paraffin—caused the intensity measured by the ionization chamber to *increase* rather than decrease. The protons, it was clear, were actually being ejected from the hydrogen atoms by the mysterious rays and propelled rapidly through the ionization chamber. *Gamma* rays were now ruled out altogether, for they would require extremely high energies, of the order of fifty million volts, in order to cause the protons to be ejected from the screen at the observed high velocities.

James Chadwick, a British physicist, solved the puzzle. It was most logical, he pointed out, that the protons were set into rapid motion by a particle of mass similar to their own. It is a well-known principle of simple mechanics that the energy transferred in a collision is greatest when the colliding particles have the same mass, as two billiard balls, for example. Thus, if the mysterious radiation should consist of such particles, it would not be necessary to assume that they had extremely high energy. Furthermore, if the particle should carry no electric charge, its great penetrating power would be explained: the electric fields of atoms would not affect its motion. By measuring the velocities with which protons were ejected from various materials and utilizing simple collision theory, it was possible for Chadwick to determine the mass of this new particle and show that it was close to the mass of the proton.

The reasoning that leads to determination of the mass of the neutron is surprisingly direct, and we can profitably consider it. When a neutron collides with a nucleus at rest and imparts momentum to it, the laws that govern the collision are the same simple ones that apply to colliding billiard balls. One law is that in a head-on collision the velocity imparted to the object struck is inversely proportional to the mass of the object plus that of the projectile. Chadwick used a thin sheet containing nitrogen and found that the velocity of the ejected nitrogen nuclei (mass 14) was only about one seventh of the velocity with which protons (mass 1) are ejected from hydrogen. This ratio of seven gives the neutron mass, M, readily, because of the inverse proportion:

$$\frac{M+14}{M+1} = 7$$

The solution of this simple equation is

$$M = 1.16$$

showing that the mass of the neutron is about 16 per cent greater than the mass of the proton. Later and more accurate measurements showed that the neutron mass is extremely close to that of the proton, exceeding it by only about one tenth of 1 per cent. Further on we shall see that this excess, tiny as it is, is of great significance.

After demonstrating the existence and measuring the mass of the new particle, Chadwick named it the *"neutron."* In fact, the name was not new; scientists had been speculating for years about the possibility of an uncharged particle with a mass about that of the proton. The most tempting possibility for the origin of such an entity had been that an electron might combine with a proton in a stable neutral configuration—something like a compressed hydrogen atom. This purely imaginary structure had been referred to as the "neutron" some dozen years before Chadwick's discovery. We know, however, that the neutron is definitely *not* a combination of a proton and an electron; the dimension of the electron rules it out. As we shall now see, the neutron is actually a fundamental particle, existing in its own right, and constituting a basic component of matter.

The Neutron and Nuclear Structure

Once the reality and mass of the neutron were established, it immediately supplied the answer to the vexing problem of nuclear structure. The difficulty associated with the excess weight of all nuclei heavier than hydrogen was simply removed by the assumption that these nuclei contained the appropriate numbers of neutrons. Thus, helium obviously would contain two protons and two neutrons in its nucleus, surrounded by two electrons. Thus the mass number of helium would be four, but the charge on its nucleus would be just two. Likewise oxygen, with a mass number of sixteen, but with a charge of only eight units, would have a nucleus containing eight neutrons and eight protons surrounded by eight electrons. Furthermore, there was no problem of the "size" of the neutron, for its large mass relative to the electron implies a much smaller wave length, enabling it to fit easily inside the nucleus. The constitution of several of the lighter nuclei in terms of neutrons and protons is shown in Figure 6.

o Neutron • Proton

Hydrogen, H^1 Beryllium, Be^9 Oxygen, O^{16}
Mass number-1   Mass number-9   Mass number-16
Charge-1   Charge-4   Charge-8

*Fig. 6. Nuclear constituents of several light atoms
are shown here stripped of their electrons. The
number of electrons surrounding each nucleus is
equal to the nuclear charge, and the normal atom
as a whole has zero charge.*

Another mystery of nuclear structure—that of *isotopes*—also was found to have a simple explanation.
It had been known for some time that atoms of a
given element—for example, chlorine—did not all
weigh exactly the same, although they had the same
chemical properties. In fact, it was possible by elab-
orate electrical and mechanical methods to separate
the atoms of a given material into classes of different and distinct weights or mass numbers. Chlorine
would divide into two definite classes of atoms, or
isotopes, some of mass number 35 and some 37. Uranium, which was comprised mainly of atoms of mass
238, was found to contain some atoms of mass 235
also. These different types of atoms of the same element, or isotopes, were very difficult to explain without the neutron, but with it there was no problem.
Clearly, the isotopes of uranium must have the same
number, 92, of protons in their nuclei, for all uranium
atoms contain 92 electrons. The heavier isotopes
simply have more neutrons, 146 in the case of U^{238},
compared with 143 for U^{235}. Actually, almost all ele-

ments have several isotopes; those of oxygen are given in Figure 7.

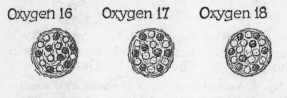

Oxygen 16   Oxygen 17   Oxygen 18

8 Protons (●)   8 Protons (●)   8 Protons (●)
8 Neutrons (○)   9 Neutrons (○)   10 Neutrons (○)
16 Mass number   17 Mass number   18 Mass number

Fig. 7. Isotopes of oxygen, each shown without its electrons, differ in mass but have identical chemical properties. Each has the same number of protons.

It was known, as well, that isotopes differing widely in weight from the common types of atoms are often unstable, and change into stable forms by emitting penetrating radiations, such as electrons or gamma rays. These *radioisotopes* were now easily explained, for they were seen to be isotopes that have an unusually large or unusually small number of neutrons. For each number of protons in the nucleus, there is a corresponding number of neutrons that will combine to produce the most stable nucleus. The most usual or stable form of the particular element contains approximately this number of neutrons. A number of neutrons much larger or much smaller than this "ideal" value will give rise to an unstable nucleus, that is, a radioisotope. As we shall learn in Chapter 5, these radioisotopes are the materials that have come into such recent tremendous importance in science, medicine, and industry, because of the great simplicity with which they can be made in large numbers in nuclear reactors. The process in which radioisotopes are made is one in which neutrons are added to stable isotopes, changing the ratio of neutrons to protons and thus causing instability.

In this chapter we have seen how the newly discovered neutron was the means of solving the long-standing problems of the existence of isotopes and the constitution of the nucleus. Already, at the beginning of its career, the tiny particle was giving a hint of its dual role as a versatile tool of pure science, invaluable as an aid to understanding the structure of matter, and as a source of innumerable practical applications, of which the production of radioisotopes was only the first. In the chapters that follow, we shall see more of the ways in which this early promise of the neutron has been fulfilled.

CHAPTER 3

Waves and Particles

Simple and straightforward as it seemed at its discovery, the neutron is now known to be a complex object. In fact, it exhibits in its behavior such a wide variety of phenomena that consideration of them all together would certainly confuse us. Several of its most important properties have been known since its discovery, of course. The fact that it was found to have a mass equal to that of the proton, but no electrical charge, was precisely what led Chadwick to conclude that he had discovered a new particle. In this chapter we are going to examine several more subtle properties—properties that will help us to understand the many ways in which the neutron has come to make itself so useful in so short a time. Many of its other fascinating qualities will gradually emerge throughout the course of this book.

It is true that at times we shall find it difficult to visualize clearly the behavior of the neutron, for it possesses the properties common to all things that are extremely small. In this subatomic world of the very small, the laws of *quantum mechanics* have full scope, and the behavior of particles seems strange to our common sense, accustomed as it is to the behavior of matter in the everyday world of large objects. Furthermore, the antics of the tiny particles within the atom—neutrons, protons, and electrons—cannot be watched directly. They are far too small for the most powerful microscopes, and their behavior must be inferred by indirect methods, so clearly exemplified by the neutron's discovery, for example.

But the indirectness of the observations makes no difference really, for we can be as certain of the existence and actions of these tiny particles as we are of such large and familiar objects as trains, planes, and ships. It is, in fact, an inspiring challenge to us to attain an understanding of the behavior of these unfamiliar and invisible objects that obey the laws of quantum mechanics, an understanding in which the ordinary rules of common sense are at times of little help—indeed, may even impede us. As a consequence of its lack of electric charge, the neutron's behavior furnishes an excellent example of these unfamiliar laws. It can move freely through matter, even at extremely low speeds where the quantum mechanical behavior, so foreign to our everyday experience, becomes most striking. In our actual experiments with these slow neutrons in the laboratory, although we cannot see them, we must think in terms of quantum mechanics constantly as we control and measure them. We do not consider their actions as some abstruse behavior of objects never experienced but as the normal behavior of the neutrons in our equipment. This behavior we simply could not describe nor understand in terms of familiar objects. Let us now look at one of the most remarkable of the neutron's characteristics, its two-sided nature as a particle *and* a wave.

Particles and Waves

Until the development of quantum mechanics, which started about 1900, it was thought that *waves* were reasonably simple and definite motions, such as

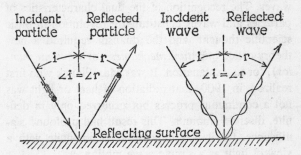

Incident
particle

Reflected
particle

Incident
wave

Reflected
wave

i   r   i   r

$\angle i = \angle r$ $\angle i = \angle r$

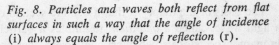

Reflecting surface

Fig. 8. Particles and waves both reflect from flat surfaces in such a way that the angle of incidence (i) always equals the angle of reflection (r).

the familiar sound and light waves. Obviously these were completely distinct from *particles,* such as electrons and protons, which were thought of as small specks of matter. Throughout the eighteenth century there had been a long controversy as to whether light was composed of waves or particles, but no one at the time ventured to suggest that *both* answers could have some truth. Of course, light waves and solid particles could at times behave in the same way, for example, when they are reflected from a flat surface (Figure 8), but this similarity was not considered to have any basic significance. Things were thought to

45

have been settled definitely when experiments on the passage of light through water "proved" that it behaved as a wave motion.

Early in the present century, however, some disquieting experiments began to reveal that light in fact exhibited some characteristics usually associated with particles; and, to add to the confusion, such definite particles as electrons were found at times to act as waves. The recognition of the dual characteristics of particles and waves constituted a revolution in basic scientific thought, and the dualism required a new theory called *quantum mechanics* (or *wave mechanics*), for its explanation. It was Max Planck who first realized, in 1900, that radiation of heat or light was not a continuous process but occurred only in definite, discrete amounts. This result had profound significance, for it was impossible to reconcile with a view of light as a simple wave motion.

The basis of the theory is that a definite section of a light wave, called a *quantum,* resembles a particle in many aspects of its behavior; conversely, that any material particle has certain wave characteristics, such as a definite *wave length*. Thus any neutron, which, of course, has a definite mass and, depending on how rapidly it is moving, a definite momentum and energy, will often act as if it is a particle, but nevertheless will show characteristics that are undeniably wavelike. This strange dualism remained unknown so long because only in the world of the very small do the quantum-mechanical effects become important. It is true that a large object—a baseball, for example—has a wave associated with it, but the wave length is so small that it is completely negligible. As a fortunate result we may without error neglect all the complications of wave behavior in dealing with baseballs.

The wave length of a particle is given by a simple formula, which we can examine profitably even though we could not hope to consider here its extensive theoretical background. It is merely

$$\lambda = \frac{h}{mv}$$

Here λ (lambda) is the wave length, m the mass, and v the velocity; h is an extremely small number called *Planck's constant*.* The form of this equation shows us that the wave length will be large if the mass and velocity are small. Because the neutron's mass is so small compared with ordinary objects, it is easy to realize that the wave length can be much larger than it would be for a baseball and hence able to produce appreciable effects of a typical wave nature. For sub-atomic particles, as shown in Figure 9, the wave length is a good estimate of the apparent "size" of the particle.

Although the mass of the neutron is very small, it is necessary that the velocity be low in order to produce significant wave-like behavior. For neutrons moving with high velocity, such as those in the experiments in which it was discovered, the wave

---

*Actually, $h = 6.63 \times 10^{-27}$ erg seconds, where "erg" is the unit of work or energy, equal to the amount of energy acquired by a mass of one gram when it is accelerated at the rate of one centimeter per second per second through a distance of one centimeter. The formula will give the wave length in centimeters if m is expressed in grams and v in centimeters per second. One erg is a very small amount of energy. A 1-ounce weight falling through 1 inch acquires an energy of about 70,000 ergs.

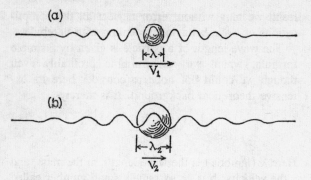

(a)

$|\leftarrow\lambda\rightarrow|$

V_1

(b)

$|\leftarrow\lambda_2\rightarrow|$

V_2

Fig. 9. Speed and wave length are related. The wave length of a particle (λ) depends on the velocity (v). The particle (b) has a larger wave length than (a) because it is moving more slowly. The higher the velocity, the shorter the wave length. In modern physics the wave length of a particle is considered to be its effective "size," which changes with velocity as shown.

length is so small that the neutrons act very much like particles. Actually, the equations we used to describe the determinations of mass treated the neutron just as if it were an everyday particle, such as a billiard ball. But when the neutron is allowed to slow down—and because of its lack of electrical charge this can be done without its being stopped completely—the wave aspects become much more important. Actually, neutrons can be slowed down to such a low velocity that they lose their particle characteristics almost completely and act as if they were waves alone, very much like sound or light.

In this chapter we shall be particularly concerned with the ways in which the behavior of very slow neutrons is so like that of ordinary light. These long wavelength neutrons can be reflected from highly polished mirrors, for example, and can be deflected as they pass into transparent materials. Their wave lengths are smaller than the wave lengths of light, it is true, but when this difference is taken into account, practically every phase of the behavior of light waves can be duplicated in experiments with slow neutrons.

The Size of Neutrons

Thus far we have not paid much attention to the precise numbers involved in the world of the very small. But now it is a good idea for us to consider the actual "sizes" of subatomic particles—the wave lengths of neutrons, and the dimensions of the atoms and nuclei with which they interact. We shall find that we have to deal with numbers almost unimaginably small compared with the ones we use every day: For example, the size of a typical atom is about 10^{-8} centimeter, which means that it would take one hundred million atoms in a row to make a line only one centimeter long, and $10^8 \times 10^8 \times 10^8$ or 10^{24} atoms to fill a cubic centimeter of solid material. Figure 10 shows that even though a gas contains far fewer atoms than a solid, the numbers are still enormous. For this reason and others, physicists who work with subatomic particles customarily measure their dimensions in units that seem very remote from the feet and inches, meters and centimeters of everyday life; but these units are used only because of their greater convenience. They can all be expressed in terms of more familiar quantities.

The velocity of an atomic particle is usually expressed in terms of its energy, and quoted in terms

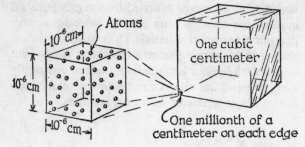

Fig. 10. Minute cube only a millionth of a centimeter on a side could contain 27 atoms of helium gas. Thus, in a cubic centimeter there would be $10^6 \times 10^6 \times 10^6 \times 27$, or 27×10^{18} atoms.

of a particular unit, the *electron volt,* or "ev." As this unit is of fundamental importance in nuclear physics, its use will aid our understanding greatly. One electron volt is the energy acquired by one electron when it is acted upon by a voltage difference of one volt. Thus, an electron as it is moved through an ordinary flashlight battery will gain an energy of about 1.5 electron volts. Likewise, as an electron passes through a 110-volt lamp, it will lose 110 electron volts of energy, this energy being converted into light and heat. Although defined in terms of the electron, the unit of energy is used for any particle or in fact for *any* kind of energy. The electron volt is very convenient in atomic and nuclear studies because the energies given to the particles are easy to relate to the energies, in volts, of the machines that accelerate the particles— the cyclotrons, cosmotrons, and bevatrons. The principle of giving energy to particles is illustrated, for a particularly low-energy example, in Figure 11. A cyclotron will produce energies of the order of several million volts, and the particles to which this energy is imparted therefore will have energies of several million electron volts, or "Mev." The last accelerator mentioned involves the unit in its very name—it produces particles of a billion electron volts energy, or "Bev."

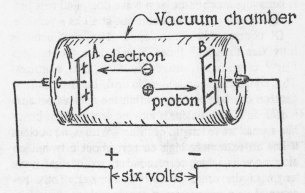

Fig. 11. "Electron volt" is an atomic unit of energy. The electric field created between the plates A and B will cause electrons to move to A and protons to B. In moving the full distance each will acquire six electron volts energy. Because of its much greater mass, the proton will move much more slowly.

But to return to the wave length of the neutron. In order that it have a wave length approximately the size of an atom, or 10^{-8} centimeter, its energy must be very much less than the million electron volts or so that would be typical of a cyclotron. In fact, the energy must be only 0.1 electron volt if the neutron is to be moving slowly enough to have a wave length of about 10^{-8} centimeter. For a neutron of this low energy it is much more meaningful to think in terms of wave rather than particle. True, the "size" of the neutron can in a sense be considered as about equal to its wave length, but we would be wrong to think of an 0.1 electron-volt neutron as a solid particle 10^{-8} cm. in extent. The neutron, as we shall see, can act as if it is this large, as large as an atom, but then it is behaving much more as a wave does, and it is better to consider it as such and not at all as a particle.

Of course, this dimension of 10^{-8} centimeter is fully ten thousand times larger than the nucleus (10^{-12} centimeter), which itself *contains* neutrons! This statement sounds paradoxical, but it is not. A neutron can be contained within the nucleus because a neutron in the nucleus is moving very rapidly, hence has a small wave length, or "size." Within the nucleus it has an extremely high energy, about fifty million electron volts, which corresponds to a very small wave length of the order of 10^{-13} centimeter. Thus, because of its great energy, it can fit within the nucleus easily.

Neutrons, whether produced in nuclear reactors or cyclotrons, usually have energies of millions of electron volts. When these neutrons are allowed to flow through matter composed of light atoms, collisions with nuclei reduce their speed until they are moving with about the same energy as the atoms of the material themselves. When this equilibrium is reached—that is, when the neutrons are "cooled" to ordinary temperature—they have energies about 0.02 electron volt and their wave length is about 2×10^{-8} centimeter. Neutrons of this energy are now supplied in copious amounts in nuclear reactors, and are used for much research in which the wave behavior of neutrons is important. We shall describe now some of the most striking ways in which the wave or optical properties of slow neutrons are observed.

Refraction

A property usually considered characteristic of wave motion is that of *refraction,* in which a beam is deflected as it passes from one material into another. Refraction is a familiar property of light; we all have learned how a beam of light is bent in passing from air into water or glass. The amount of bending that occurs is determined by the *index of refraction* of each material. The index of water is about 1.3, of glass about 1.5, and for air it is extremely close to unity, being exactly unity for a vacuum.

These values of the index tell us in a rather direct manner the amount by which a beam of light will be bent as it passes from air into a particular substance. As shown in Figure 12, the bending is given by the equation:

$$\frac{\sin i}{\sin r} = n$$

where i is the *angle of incidence,* r the *angle of refraction,* and n the index of refraction of the material. From this equation we see that a beam of light will bend so as to be closer to the normal as it enters glass, or any dense material, as in Figure 12, and, conversely, will bend away from the normal as it leaves.

For a neutron, the same relationships apply. Passage of a neutron beam into a material will produce a bending in the same way. The major difference in the refraction of light from the refraction of neutrons is that the bending of the beam of neutrons is much smaller than for light; that is, the index of refraction is much closer to unity, typically differing from it by only 0.1 per cent. Nevertheless, the small bendings, or refractions, that occur for neutrons actually can be demonstrated experimentally. Of course, it is necessary to select a material that is reasonably "transparent" to neutrons to demonstrate refraction. Glass and water are not transparent in this sense, but fortunately there are a few materials, such as the metals

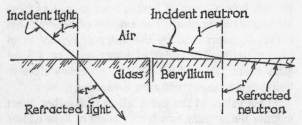

Fig. 12. Light and neutrons both have the property of refraction. When a beam of light or a beam of neutrons enters a dense material—glass for light and beryllium for neutrons, for example—it bends. The bending is much less for neutrons and in the opposite direction.

beryllium and bismuth, that are. Careful measurements show that a neutron beam usually bends in the *opposite* direction relative to light; in other words, the index (of most materials) for neutrons is *less* than unity. The main characteristics of refraction of light and neutrons are compared in Figure 12; the transparent material is glass for light and beryllium for neutrons.

There is one special case in which neutrons are very strongly refracted, although the effect is hard to observe. If our equipment is sensitive enough so that we can watch what happens as a neutron enters the nucleus of an atom, we shall be able to see very marked refraction effects.

Since almost all the mass of an atom is concentrated inside the tiny nucleus, its density is very great. As a result of this great density, the index of refraction of the nucleus for neutrons is markedly different from unity; in fact, it is comparable to the index of refraction of glass for light. The situations are not quite the same, for the wave length of the neutron is not small relative to the nucleus, as is the wave length of light relative to a glass lens. But it turns out that this difference in relative scale merely complicates the refraction of neutrons by nuclei to a certain extent, without changing the basic situation.

In order to study the way in which neutron paths are bent as they pass through nuclei, it is necessary to use high-energy neutrons whose wave lengths are smaller than the nuclei themselves. If their wave lengths were larger than the nuclei, the neutrons would be scattered diffusely, as light is scattered by minute dust particles, and no refraction effect would be observed. As we have seen, a neutron of size comparable to a nucleus has about a million electron volts of energy; at this energy it behaves like a particle in most respects, but to some extent its wavelike characteristics are still present. The behavior of neutrons of this energy as they pass through nuclei furnishes a powerful means of studying the sizes, shapes, and structures of the nuclei. Later in this book we shall look in a little more detail at experiments of this type; at the moment, we wish merely to emphasize that a beam of neutrons is refracted in a way very similar to the way in which light is refracted, provided that

the indexes of refraction of the refracting materials
have similar values.

Neutron Mirrors

One of the most striking demonstrations of the
neutrons' similarity to light waves is their reflection
by mirror surfaces. The reflection is best shown under conditions in which all the neutrons are reflected,
with none entering the mirror. We should recall first
the conditions for such *total reflection,* for example
in the familiar case of light passing through glass. As
the index of refraction of glass for light is greater than
unity, it follows from Figure 12 that total reflection
occurs when a light ray is incident on a polished glass
surface from *within* the glass, as shown in Figure 13.

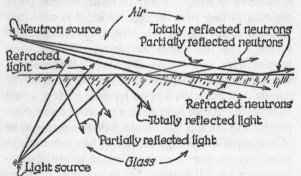

*Fig. 13. Another similarity between the behavior of
light and neutrons is illustrated here. Both have the
properties of partial and total reflection, but the
source of light must be inside the reflecting surface
while the source of neutrons must be outside. There
is a critical angle below which there is complete reflection and above which there is partial reflection
and partial transmission with refraction.*

The beam of light must strike the surface within a certain range of angles in order to be totally reflected; light incident perpendicular to the surface will pass out of the glass. The limiting angle for which the reflection is total is called the *critical angle,* and its value can easily be calculated from the index of refraction by setting the angle r equal to 90 degrees.

One distinct difference in the total reflection of neutrons and of light arises because most materials have an index less than unity for neutrons but greater than unity for light. As a result, neutrons will reflect totally from a polished glass surface if they are incident on the surface from *outside* the glass, just the reverse of the situation for light. We see another distinction in Figure 13: the range of possible angles for total reflection with neutrons is much less than for light. The index is so close to unity that the angle at which the neutrons meet the glass must be less than one degree to attain total reflection. Because of the limited angles and the much shorter wave length of neutrons, it is much harder to make a neutron mirror than a mirror for light. Nevertheless, as first shown by Enrico Fermi, it is possible to reflect neutrons from mirrors made of many materials if sufficient care is taken to make the mirror's surface extremely flat. Actually, an extremely flat surface can be attained by use of liquid mirrors. For example, a neutron beam can be totally reflected from a surface of liquid mercury if the mercury is kept undisturbed to avoid ripples.

The mirror reflection is a vivid proof indeed that slow neutrons have strong wave characteristics. For example, the critical angle depends on the properties of the mirror material averaged over many atoms, not on any particular atom. If the material, like iron, contains many small crystal grains, each neutron will reflect with the same critical angle just as if variations from grain to grain did not exist. This behavior is striking when we remember that the wave length of the neutron is so small compared to the individual crystal grains, the latter being perhaps ten thousand times larger than the neutron wave length. The explanation is that the neutron in reflecting from the mirror does not behave as a particle, but instead as a very extended wave, reflecting from *all* the atoms in the entire surface, even though it is several inches across. This behavior is very different from what we might expect of small particles: each would hit a particular spot on the mirror.

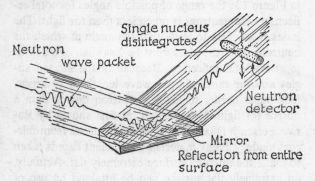

Fig. 14. Wave and particle behavior of the neutron can be demonstrated in a single experiment. The neutron acts as a wave in spreading over the entire mirror surface, yet is recorded in the detector as a particle.

Yet, in the same experiment, as shown in Figure 14, we find the neutrons acting as if they are indeed tiny particles. Now our "common sense" is confused indeed. The reflected neutrons are observed by means of a neutron "counter" in which each neutron interacts with a *single* nucleus. By disintegrating, the nucleus reveals the neutron's presence. The mirror-reflection experiment brings us face to face with the fundamental principles of quantum mechanics—and with the puzzling behavior of the world of the very small. The manner in which a neutron can act as an extended wave when it reflects from the mirror surface, yet immediately thereafter interact with a single nucleus, is a dramatic demonstration of the essential duality of all matter. We must face the fact that the neutrons at one and the same time can display wave and particle characteristics, disrupting as this may be to our normal experience. To reconcile these two apparently contradictory phases of the behavior of matter was the great accomplishment of quantum mechanics.

By studying the very slow neutrons, we have seen striking examples of how the principles of wave mechanics, so unlike our everyday experience, rule the behavior of tiny particles. Wave mechanical properties are not visible in things as we observe them with our eyes, but the ultimate practical results of these properties, such as electric atomic-power stations, are dramatic indeed. The large-scale results could never have been produced without a thorough knowledge of those underlying principles.

CHAPTER 4

Inside the Neutron

The first important characteristics of the neutron to be investigated were its mass, lack of electrical charge, and its place in nuclear structure. So far in our story of the neutron we have considered these properties briefly but have not penetrated within the neutron itself, so to speak, to investigate the possibility that it may be composed of still other particles. In actual fact, although the first investigations did not reveal any complexity, later developments showed that the neutron was by no means a simple particle that could not be further divided.

When only the first few facts about neutrons, protons, and nuclei were known, it was thought that neutrons and protons were "fundamental particles." That is, they were believed to be fundamental to the structure of all matter yet simple within themselves, beyond the possibility of being broken down into more basic components. This idea of ultimate, simple, unalterable particles has always been attractive, but just as do atoms and again nuclei, neutrons and protons indeed have an inner structure—furthermore, one that can be altered profoundly. But in spite of this inner complexity, it is still true that the neutron and the proton are, in a real sense, fundamental and simple particles. They are fundamental because they are the basic building blocks from which all matter is constructed and they exemplify simply and directly the laws of quantum mechanics obeyed by all matter.

Some of these laws we already have seen at work in our examination of the wave properties of the neutron, but we have not taken into account its actual structure. Now we shall investigate the interior. By studying the constitution of the neutron itself, we are analyzing matter stripped of many of its complications, and therefore perhaps we can see more clearly the underlying laws of nature. This possibility of gaining information of wide validity by studying a "simple" thing was well put by Tennyson:

> Flower in the crannied wall,
> I pluck you out of the crannies,
> I hold you here, root and all, in my hand,
> Little flower—but *if* I could understand
> What you are, root and all, and all in all,
> I should know what God and man is.

We realize, of course, that the flower is indeed no *simple* object. Neither, we shall find, is our neutron, a tiny component of the little flower. Although we cannot hope ever to see the neutron as we can the flower, we can learn to appreciate the wonder and the beauty of its inner structure.

The Neutron Disintegrates

Already we have considered the mass of the neutron—about 0.1 per cent greater than the proton—and hinted that this slight excess implied important consequences. The slight difference in mass opened the possibility that the neutron would be unstable and would disintegrate spontaneously into a proton, at the same time releasing energy. Because of the equivalence of mass and energy, predicted by Albert Einstein in 1905 as a consequence of his theory of relativity, the neutron can be thought of as having more energy than the proton. In changing to the proton some mass would disappear, which would represent considerable energy even though constituting such a small fraction of the proton's mass.

Einstein's basic equation, $E = mc^2$, does not predict at all the particular process by which mass can be changed into energy, nor in what form the released energy will appear. It does tell, however, the exact amount of energy that would result in such a transformation.* The spontaneous change of a heavier into a lighter nucleus, with release of energy, had been known since the discovery of *radioactivity* of heavy elements about 1900. The amount of energy released in these transformations is given exactly by Einstein's simple equation; m, the mass converted into energy, is the difference between the mass of the original atom and the one into which it changed.

Consequently, the change of a neutron into a proton, should it occur, would be an example of the simplest possible radioactive transformation. Almost certainly, an electron would be released in the process, thus leaving the proton with its expected positive

*The amount is so large because c, the velocity of light, is 3×10^{10} centimeters per second. If m is one pound (453 grams), the energy will be 4×10^{23} ergs or 11 billion kilowatt hours!

charge. Although there seemed to be no reason to question these arguments, it could not be predicted how long neutrons would exist before the release. But with Einstein's equation the amount of energy given up in the transformation could be calculated easily from the difference in mass of the neutron and the proton, an energy that is about one million electron volts.

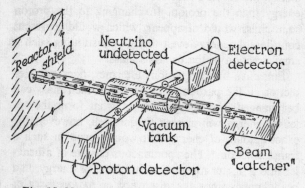

Fig. 15. Neutron disintegration, not yet fully understood, is studied in this experimental arrangement. Disintegration produces a proton and an electron, which can be detected if they travel in the directions shown. The mysterious neutrino passes away undetected.

Because there were not many neutrons available for experiments in the first years after the neutron's discovery, there seemed little chance to observe this most fundamental form of radioactivity. Somewhat later, however, when large nuclear reactors started operating, enormous numbers of neutrons became available. These are the neutrons produced by the chain reaction within the reactor, and they emerge from the reactor through a hole in the surrounding shield as a "beam" of free neutrons. With so many neutrons in the beam, some, if the theory held, probably would disintegrate while passing an appropriate detecting instrument just outside the reactor, and it would be possible to observe the phenomenon.

The disintegration was shown to take place. In the experiment two detectors, one sensitive to electrons, the other to protons, were placed on opposite sides of the neutron beam, as sketched in Figure 15. By observing that at times an electron appeared in one instrument and in the other a proton was simultaneously detected, the experimenters proved that the neutron did decay in the manner expected. In fact, careful measurements of the electrons and protons revealed another important aspect of the neutron-disintegration process.

If the electron and the proton were the *only* products, they always would be found moving in exactly opposite directions—in accord with the fundamental law of mechanics, the conservation of momentum. (Momentum is the product of the mass of a body and its instantaneous velocity. Since momentum has direction, it is a vector quantity, not a simple magnitude, and is subject to graphical or trigonometrical solutions. The conservation law says that in a closed system in which bodies act upon one another, the individual motions may change, but the vector sum of all the momenta remains constant.)

The behavior of the products of the disintegration, or "explosion," of the neutron indicated either that the process did not satisfy the law or that some of the energy was being carried away by a mysterious third particle. Since physicists are as reluctant to abandon the law of the conservation of momentum as they would be to give up other basic laws, such as the conservation of energy, the existence of a mysterious third particle of zero charge and zero mass was postulated. The Italian physicist Enrico Fermi named it the neutrino, or "little neutron." Because the neutrino does lack charge and mass, little is known of the particle itself. But the neutrino's presence in the neutron disintegration is revealed—only indirectly, it is true—by the very fact that the electron and proton are *not* always emitted, as the conservation law says they should be, in exactly opposite directions. This method of ferreting out the existence of a neutrino is a highly significant illustration of the indirect way in which today's physicists go about their exciting business.

The energy produced in the neutron-disintegration process could be determined as well, and it proved to be the same for each disintegration, provided that due allowance was made for the energy carried away by the neutrino. The energy was found to be just the amount computed from the neutron-proton mass difference, about one million electron volts. Furthermore, the number of disintegrations detected compared with the number of neutrons in the beam gave the average length of time a neutron lasts before decaying—about ten minutes. This relatively long lifetime explains why transformations of neutrons were not observed in the early experiments.

The situation obviously is vastly different for neutrons inside a nucleus, for if neutrons should last there only ten minutes before turning into protons, nuclei would soon be all protons and all matter would cease to be stable. However, it is only free neutrons, away from the influence of other nuclear particles, that suffer radioactive disintegration. Within a nucleus, a neutron is profoundly affected by neighboring particles, and, while rapid changes may actually take place, the total numbers of neutrons and protons within the nucleus remains firmly fixed.

But to return to the disintegration of the free neutron, we must consider a very pertinent question concerning the origin of the electron: How does an electron originate in a neutron, which certainly does not contain electrons? In many cases of decay of radioisotopes we have the same problem; electrons emerge in the disintegration from nuclei in which, as we already have seen, no electron could be present. The structure of the neutron must indeed be more complex than was imagined shortly after its discovery. Electrons could not possibly exist inside neutrons, but somehow they must be produced from the constituents of the neutron during the act of disintegration itself.

A few years after discovery of the neutron, it was learned that neutrons always have associated with them lighter particles called *mesons*. The meson had been predicted on purely theoretical grounds in 1936 by the Japanese physicist, H. Yukawa, to explain the enormous forces within nuclei. These mesons, of mass about one seventh that of the neutron (but about three hundred times the electron mass), have a very evanescent existence and are continually being created from the mass of the neutron and absorbed back into it, without escaping from the structure. A meson, *if separated* from nuclear particles, disintegrates almost immediately, and about a millionth of a second later it has become an electron and a neutrino. While we cannot hope to consider here the de-

67

tails of the neutron disintegration, and indeed the process is only dimly understood at present, it is easy to see that mesons provide the key to an explanation. Mesons exist associated with or actually "in" neutrons, not normally leaving them altogether. On the other hand, electrons cannot do so because of their smaller mass, hence larger "size." The electron is created from the meson in the process of the disintegration of the neutron, in a manner similar to the decay of a meson separated from neutrons.

The association of mesons with neutrons is not merely a hypothesis invoked to explain the emission of electrons—there are other properties of neutrons that reveal the existence and some of the essential properties of these ever-present mesons. We shall consider now one result of the structure of the neutron that is compelling proof for the presence of mesons therein.

The Neutron as a Magnet

We do not think of most common materials as magnetic, because the magnetic fields associated with them are extremely weak. But a few metals, the most familiar of which is iron, can become strong magnets. A bar of iron may be magnetized intensely by placing it inside a coil of wire carrying a heavy electric current. The bar will then show typical magnetic effects: It will attract pieces of iron and will align itself parallel to the earth's magnetic field, as a compass needle does, if allowed to rotate freely.

The neutron itself is surrounded by a magnetic field, and is in effect a small magnet having many of the characteristics of the magnetized bar of iron. The neutron was shown to be a magnet by simple experiments in which sheets of iron were placed in neutron beams to study the number of neutrons penetrating the sheets. The penetration of neutrons through the iron was found to be markedly different, depending whether the iron was magnetized or not. It is easy to see that this result proves that the neutron is a magnet. Magnetization of the iron affects only the magnetic fields around the iron atoms, the nuclei remaining the same. Thus the measured changes of neutron intensity with magnetization of the iron proved that the neutron is affected strongly by the magnetic fields of the iron atoms. For this to happen, the neutron itself must have a magnetic field surrounding it, hence be a magnet itself. Otherwise no interaction would have been observed.

The neutron is *electrically* neutral, but this fact by no means implies that there can be no *magnetization,* even though magnetic fields are produced by moving electric charges. Within the iron bar the motion of electrons in atoms constitutes the moving charges that produce the magnetic field. Yet each atom as a whole is electrically neutral because the electron charges are just balanced by the positive charges on the nuclei of the iron atoms. The situation in the neutron, as illustrated in Figure 16, is analogous. Here the moving charge is the meson associated with the neutron. The meson, charged negatively, circulates within the neutron, constituting an electric current and thus giving rise to the neutron's magnetic field. As the neutron is electrically neutral, there must be a positive charge left in the center of the neutron when the meson is moving in its orbit.

In the magnetism of the neutron we thus find

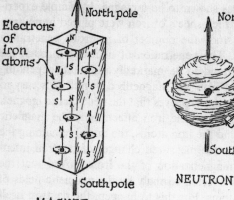

Fig. 16. *Magnetism of the neutron is analogous to magnetization of an iron bar. In both, moving electrical charges produce the magnetic fields. In iron, electrons constitute the current; in neutrons, it is the negatively charged meson. The neutron's magnetism is another evidence of its complexity.*

additional strong evidence for the complexity of the neutron, in particular for its existence, at least part of the time, as a positive central core surrounded by a negative meson. The disintegration of the neutron, leaving a residual proton, suggests strongly that the positive core required to explain the magnetic field is the proton itself. In addition, the measured strength of the magnetic field of the neutron gives some rough information concerning the time that the neutron exists in the separated state, as meson surrounding proton. This state of affairs lasts for only a small percentage of the time, but it is sufficient for establishment of a definite magnetic effect. The details of the processes by which the meson can produce the magnetic field and also, after a life of some ten minutes, give rise to an electron and neutrino, are far from being completely understood, and solving the problems calls for much intense effort. But these details are basic to the understanding, "all in all," of neutrons, protons, atoms, and molecules.

Polarized Neutrons

As we all know, a magnet has a definite sense of direction associated with it. One end is the *north pole,* the other the *south pole,* so named because of the direction the magnet will point if allowed to turn freely. The south pole of one magnet will repel that of another magnet, but attract its north pole. As a neutron is a small magnet, we may well expect similar behavior. Indeed, just those properties we associate with magnets are clearly exhibited by neutrons, and their manifestations supply valuable information concerning the neutron's structure and the magnetism of atoms as well.

Like a magnet, a neutron "points" in some direction, and in a beam of neutrons emerging from a nuclear reactor the neutrons are oriented at random: they point in every direction. However, it is possible by various methods to align the neutrons so they point in a single direction; we then say that we have a beam of *polarized neutrons.* The production and properties of such beams of polarized neutrons have many close analogies to polarized light, although the fundamental mechanism actually is different. Polarization of light refers to the direction of vibration of the electric and magnetic fields that represent light, while a polarized neutron is one in which the direction of magnetization has a definite orientation. Nevertheless, the simple properties of polarized neutrons and of polarized light are similar. The beams are produced in a polarizer, studied in an analyzer, and the direction of polarization can be changed by analogous means.

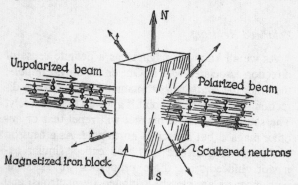

Fig. 17. Polarized neutrons can be produced by passing a neutron beam through highly magnetized iron. The iron scatters neutrons whose fields point in the same direction as the iron's. Neutrons oriented oppositely are transmitted. If the block is sufficiently thick, a strongly polarized beam results.

The simplest way of producing polarized neutrons is to allow a beam of slow neutrons to pass through a sheet of iron that is highly magnetized. The method is illustrated in Figure 17. Within the iron, the neutrons pointing in the same direction as the magnetization of the iron atoms are repelled and scattered out of the beam; the other neutrons pass through the iron more easily. In this way, provided the sheet of iron is sufficiently thick (several inches), the emerging neutrons, pointing *predominantly* in a direction op-

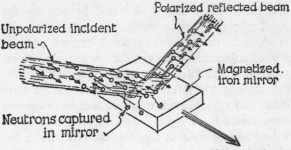

Fig. 18. Magnetized mirror can be used to produce a completely polarized neutron beam, as illustrated here. Neutrons oriented in the direction of the mirror's field are totally reflected. The others penetrate the mirror and so leave the beam.

posite to that of the magnetization of the iron, will be strongly polarized. A beam of *completely polarized* neutrons can be produced by reflection from a mirror, using the technique of total reflection described in the last chapter. If the mirror (Figure 18) is magnetized and the beam hits it at just the correct angle, the neutrons pointing in the direction of magnetization of the mirror will reflect, but the others will penetrate the mirror and not reflect at all. As a result, the neutrons in the reflected beam *all* point in the direction of magnetization and constitute a completely polarized beam.

Beams of polarized neutrons can be used to explore in a direct manner the magnetic structure of iron or similar materials. The neutrons, passing through the individual atoms, penetrate deeply into the iron. In the process they are affected by the magnetic fields of individual atoms, not merely by the average of many atoms, as would be true for the usual magnetic measurements. By studying the way in which the neutrons are deflected, changed in direction of polarization, or even depolarized, we can investigate the detailed shape of the magnetic field inside the iron. The information obtained is much more direct and unambiguous than was learned from most older methods. A typical method, for example, involved measurement of the magnetic field outside the object, but the results could reveal only average properties of the atomic magnetic fields. Polarized neutrons have also made it possible to determine with high accuracy the strength of the neutron's own magnetic field; this is done by studying the magnetic fields necessary to depolarize a neutron beam. The neutron's field has a direct bearing on the theory of the meson structure of the neutron, our next object of attention.

The Structure of the Neutron

Thus far we have presented no direct evidence for the details of the actual structure of the neutron, of the central positively charged core and the circulating negative meson. Instead, we have had recourse to the meson to explain the observed properties of the neutron, primarily the magnetic field surrounding it and its disintegration into a proton and an electron. While it would be extremely difficult to explain these characteristics without the meson, they do not *prove* at all that the particular structure we have imagined (Figure 19) is the correct one.

It should be possible to demonstrate this structure by a reasonably direct experiment. The situation is

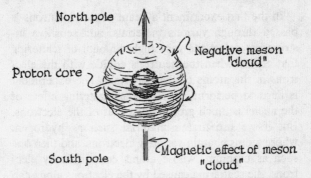

North pole

Negative meson "cloud"

Proton core

South pole

Magnetic effect of meson "cloud"

Fig. 19. Internal structure of the neutron is far from simple, and we know little about it. The evidence seems to support this picture of one aspect of neutron behavior. For a small fraction of the time, the neutron separates into a positively charged core (proton) surrounded by a circulating negative meson "cloud."

closely analogous to that of an atom, shown by Rutherford's experiment to consist of a massive, positively charged central core surrounded by negative electrons. Unfortunately, it is much more difficult to do the Rutherford type of experiment for the neutron: first, because we do not have large numbers of neutrons in the free state to bombard with charged particles; and, second, because we would require very high-energy (hence "small") particles to fit inside the neutron. Recently it has been possible, however, to get some direct information on the internal structure of the neutron by two types of experiments. Unfortunately, the two results seem at first sight to be contradictory, and the problem of reconciling them is being vigorously attacked at the present time by theoretical physicists.

In the first experiment a beam of slow neutrons is passed through various materials, and sensitive instruments detect the very slight amount of scattering that occurs when the neutrons collide with the electrons in the atoms of the materials. The experiment is hard to perform, because the scattering effect of the nuclei is much greater than that of the electrons. But if we use first a material such as hydrogen, whose atoms contain very few electrons, and then one such as uranium, whose atoms contain many electrons, the scattering caused by the electrons alone can be identified.

As we might expect, an interaction is observed between the magnetic field of the neutron, created by the circulating meson, and the magnetic fields of the atoms of the material, created by the electrons. This is just the well-known magnetic interaction that is used to polarize neutrons. The amazing thing is that no additional *electrical* interaction is observed, the one that is expected when the neutron and electron are so close that the electron is "inside" the neutron—that is, between the meson and the central positive core of the neutron to which it should be attracted. This result is as astonishing as if Rutherford had found no scattering of alpha particles when they passed inside the electron shells of the atoms and were exposed to the positive nuclear charge.

From this "neutron-electron" experiment we are forced to conclude that there is no central spot of positive electricity within the neutron distinct from the surrounding negative charge of the meson. Instead, the neutron must be nearly neutral electrically throughout its volume! But before considering whether there is hope of reconciling this result with the other properties of the neutron, let us turn briefly to the second experiment that also gives some direct information concerning the interior of the neutron.

In this experiment high-speed electrons of several hundred million electron-volts energy are used to bombard neutrons. Since we have no free neutrons available for targets, the best we can do is to perform an indirect experiment, comparing the effect of ordinary hydrogen as the target with that of "heavy hydrogen" or *deuterium*. The deuterium nucleus consists of one neutron and one proton, whereas the ordinary hydrogen nucleus is, of course, the proton alone. Thus we can be reasonably confident that the difference in results in the two cases is the same as if we had scattered electrons from the neutron alone. The results of this experiment agree with the first one, for there is no *electrical* effect when the bombarding electron passes through the neutron—there is no evidence of a positive central core separated from the negative meson. However, in the electron-scattering experiment, it is also possible to measure the distance through which the *magnetic* structure of the neutron extends; this distance is found to be about 10^{-13} centimeter, about that expected for the size of the meson's orbit around the center of the neutron.

The paradox that we face at present concerning the structure of the neutron is a direct consequence of these experiments: It now seems that there is no finite extension of negative electrical charge around a positive center but that the region producing its magnetic field does extend over a finite distance. The magnetic effects of the neutron are produced, we feel sure, by the motion of the meson as it circulates around the center; hence, it is reasonable that the magnetic core is found to extend a distance, about 10^{-13} centimeters, equal to that expected for the size of a meson's orbit. But there seems to be no sharp localization of positive charge at the center of the neutron, in spite of the fact that the neutron as a whole is electrically neutral! The neutron structure, with a negatively charged meson circulating in it to produce its extended magnetic core, yet with no evident separation of negative charge from a positive center, is one of the great mysteries of modern physics.

While it is a dangerous procedure to imagine simple models familiar to our usual senses in an attempt to explain properties of subatomic particles, let us for clarity mention a possibility that might at least be a clue to the answer. It may be that the neutron is a particle with a central core of *uncharged* matter surrounded, not by one meson, but by several. These mesons would have to be both positive and negative but of equal numbers so that the total charge would be zero. If the positive and negative mesons circulated in *opposite* directions around the central core, their magnetic fields would add but their electrical effects would cancel. Of course, constructing an adequate theory involves much more than this crude suggestion. It is a matter of precise calculations of the possibility of mesons existing in pairs and the stability of such a system—matters far beyond the things that we can hope to discuss here.

In this chapter we have seen that although the neutron is a fundamental particle in the sense that it is one of the basic building blocks of almost all atoms, it is far from being fundamental in the sense of being inherently simple. Indeed, we hardly can claim to understand even the most elementary facts about the inner structure of the neutron. But, despite the many gaps in our knowledge, we are able to describe with great accuracy, and in great detail, the manner in which neutrons interact with protons, nuclei, and atoms. In treating these interactions we make no error if we think of the neutron as a simple and structure-less particle—uncharged, with a definite mass and a wave length depending on its energy. In the following chapters we shall see some of the ways in which the neutron is used as a powerful tool for investigating the structure of matter. As we do so, we shall revert once more to thinking of the neutron as a simple particle. It is fortunate that we can, for we have learned that inside the neutron our view is dim indeed.

CHAPTER 5

Nuclei and Neutrons

After our brief glimpse of the complicated inner structure of the neutron, with its mesons continually being emitted and re-absorbed, we turn now to the fascinating things that occur when neutrons meet other matter. For all the rich range of phenomena observed in the interaction with nuclei, atoms, molecules, and crystals, neutrons act as simple uncharged particles, of definite mass, wave length, and magnetic strength; the interior complexity is not revealed. Of the many forms of matter with which neutrons have important interactions, we shall confine ourselves at present to the nuclei of atoms alone. The great value of the neutron as a tool was first shown by these interactions with nuclei: they have enabled men to transform nuclei readily, making nuclei of striking new properties and in great abundance. In addition, the nuclear effects of neutrons furnish a wide variety of basic information. Let us consider several striking examples.

Nuclear Capture of Slow Neutrons

Because of their lack of charge, neutrons can slip inside atoms easily, being very little affected by the electrons surrounding the nucleus, and can reach the very surface of the latter. Close to the positively charged nucleus the electric field is extremely strong; hence, a proton, being strongly repelled, could reach the nucleus only if moving very rapidly. But this intense electrical field essentially has no effect on the neutron; however slowly it may be moving, it can reach the nucleus.

The neutron may bounce off the nuclear surface, but it also can enter the nucleus, be absorbed by it, and by a very striking change make its absorption known. A moment's thought will enable us to see how the neutron's "capture" is manifested. Absorption of a neutron into the nucleus of an atom does not change the chemical nature of the atom; for the addition of a neutron merely produces another *isotope* of the same chemical element. Thus ordinary aluminum (written Al^{27}) after absorption of a neutron becomes aluminum-28 (Al^{28}) with one additional unit of weight but with no change in ordinary *chemical* properties. On the other hand, the change within the nucleus is extremely great: Al^{27} has great stability, but the Al^{28} atom is *radioactive* and emits an energetic electron called a *beta* ray. The important nuclear changes that have occurred in this chain of events are sketched in Figure 20.

The energy given off in the form of the rapidly moving beta ray comes from the mass that is added

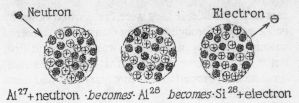

Al^{27} + neutron ·*becomes*· Al^{28} *becomes*·Si^{28} + electron

Al^{27} $\begin{cases} 13 \text{ protons} \\ 14 \text{ neutrons} \end{cases}$ Al^{28} $\begin{cases} 13 \text{ protons} \\ 15 \text{ neutrons} \end{cases}$ Si^{28} $\begin{cases} 14 \text{ protons} \\ 14 \text{ neutrons} \end{cases}$

   Stable   Unstable   Stable

*Fig. 20. Nuclear changes resulting when stable alu-
minum (Al^{27}) absorbs a neutron are illustrated
here. The unstable aluminum radioisotope, Al^{28}, is
formed. It decays by emitting one electron, and
silicon (Si^{28}) is created.*

when the neutron is absorbed. Part of the added mass
is converted into energy when the radioactive particle
is emitted, and as we know, loss of a very small
amount of mass produces a great deal of energy. Soon
we shall discuss the tremendous significance to science, medicine, and industry of the radioactivity resulting from neutron capture, but at the moment we
are interested only in the fact that neutron absorption
can be readily detected by the later emission of radiation from the capturing nucleus.

Conversion of stable atoms into radioactive forms
by means of capture of neutrons is a phenomenon of
basic importance and one that can be easily observed.
As a result, many scientists started studying the capture of neutrons in nuclei very soon after the discovery
of the neutron itself. One of these was Enrico Fermi,
who, with a small group of physicists in Italy, found
a property of neutron behavior that was most surprising. The neutrons were much *more* likely to be

captured by nuclei if they were first slowed down by
being passed through water or some other material
containing hydrogen atoms. It was puzzling at first,
but it soon became apparent that one of the most
fundamental properties of tiny particles had been
clearly demonstrated.

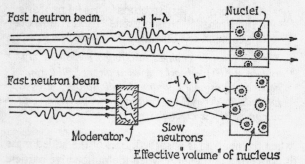

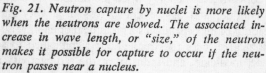

*Fig. 21. Neutron capture by nuclei is more likely
when the neutrons are slowed. The associated increase in wave length, or "size," of the neutron
makes it possible for capture to occur if the neutron passes near a nucleus.*

The reason for the increased efficacy of the neutron
in making nuclear reactions was a definite sign that
the wave length of the neutron, which, as we have
seen, is in effect its size, increases as it moves more
slowly. The increase in rate of neutron capture by the
nuclei was a definite and most dramatic illustration
that the neutron, discovered in terms of its particle
characteristics, could behave equally well as a wave.
As the neutron moves more slowly, its wave length
increases, or in other words it becomes larger. It is
not at all surprising that the larger the neutron, the
more chance it has of hitting the nucleus and being

absorbed. Figure 21 illustrates that the nucleus is in effect surrounded by a large volume in which slow neutrons can be captured, one that can be enormous relative to the actual nuclear volume. These early neutron experiments were definite verification of the wave properties predicted by quantum mechanics.

Aided by the discovery that slowing the neutrons would increase their chance of absorption by nuclei, Fermi and his helpers soon found that almost every element could be made radioactive by bombardment with neutrons. In addition to demonstrating the quantum mechanical properties of particles, capture of slow neutrons has proved to be of enormous value because of the radioactive materials thereby produced. These radioactive materials, or *radioisotopes,* now are available on a large scale, because of the enormous number of neutrons present in nuclear reactors, and, as we shall see, have manifold applicability as scientific tools.

Radioisotopes

With the tremendous neutron intensities resulting from the chain reaction, which we shall describe later, isotopes in quantities unknown in the early days of neutron research now can be produced. Many of these radioisotopes at the present time are made in a large nuclear reactor at Oak Ridge, Tennessee, whence they are shipped throughout the world to research centers, hospitals, and industries.

The manifold uses of radioisotopes are based on the penetrating radiations they emit, thus allowing their whereabouts to be "traced" with considerable precision. In the principal uses radioisotopes function

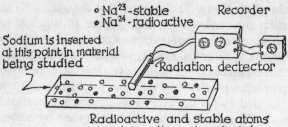

Fig. 22. Radioisotope "tracers" are immensely valuable products of neutron interactions. They are used in scientific investigations, horticulture, industrial processes, and medicine. The tracer's progress through the body, through a plant, or through the stages of an experiment or process can be followed. Here the tracer sodium (Na^{24}), usually mixed with stable sodium (Na^{23}), is introduced into the tank at one end. Its progress through the tank can be detected.

as "tracers." The radiations from disintegrating nuclei, detected in radiation "counters," are used to detect the presence of the atoms of radioisotope in the material under study, as shown in Figure 22, whether it be a chemical reaction, living tissue, or some industrial process. In delicate and precise ways the radiations from tracers reveal their presence, atom by atom, and provide us with information we could not get with older methods. Thus they show how elements participate in chemical reactions; how fertilizers move through the roots of plants and throughout the stem and leaves; how important elements of food are taken into the body and eventually get into the tissues; and how any desired component operates in an industrial process. Fantastically tiny amounts of material, much smaller than a millionth of a gram, can be traced through a process that is completely inaccessible by ordinary means. There is hardly a field of science, medicine, or engineering that is not being advanced at present by these potent tools—radioisotopes used as tracers.

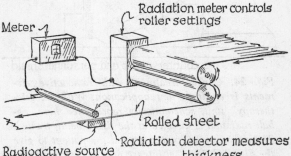

Fig. 23. Radioactive gauge measures the thickness of sheet metal as it goes through the rolling process. The amount of radiation getting through the sheet tells its thickness. The measurement is automatically fed to motors that adjust the separation of the rollers to keep the metal thickness constant.

In the large field of industrial control the radiations of the radioisotopes are used to measure the thickness of materials, to test for the presence of various components in chemical processes, and by these means to control rapid and continuous industrial processes. As an example, the mode of operation of a "thickness gauge" to maintain control of the rolling of sheet material is depicted in Figure 23.

Still another field of use of radioisotopes—the most dramatic of all—is the treatment of disease. As tracers, radioisotopes are used not only to study the normal

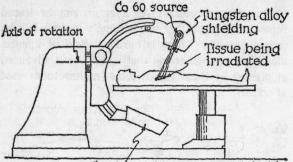

Fig. 24. Cancer treatment with radioactive elements is an important application. With a "teletherapy" unit, schematically represented here, cobalt radiation is directed at the tissue being treated. The apparatus is rotated around the patient to give the diseased tissue an intense dose and to minimize damage to healthy tissue.

functions of living tissue but also to diagnose disease. Moreover, it is possible to treat various forms of cancer by direct application of the lethal radiations. Capable of killing many cells when sufficiently intense, they can be used to control the malignant growth of several types of cancer cells. The treatment is much like that used for years with radium, but now that every chemical element can be made radioactive, the scope and the variety are vastly increased. An apparatus is illustrated in Figure 24. Radioactive cobalt, for example, can be used externally, or placed inside the body in the form of wire or beads to treat cancers of specific tissues, methods much more versatile than radium techniques had been.

In pure research, medical treatment, and industry the applications of radioisotopes, remarkable already, will expand in a manner that is impossible to estimate. Even from a dollar-and-cents standpoint the gains are amazing; at this writing the Atomic Energy Commission has estimated that in industry alone savings of half a billion dollars yearly already have been gained through use of radioisotopes. It is impossible, of course, to put a monetary value on the countless forms of research in which radioisotopes are used, or on medical treatment, but it is certain that here the ultimate benefit to human welfare will far outstrip the industrial economic gains.

As radioisotopes can kill living cells, great care must be taken in their use. However, it is indeed fortunate that modern radiation-detection instruments have great sensitivity; the amounts of radioisotopes used as tracers can be kept so small that no harm results from radiation. In treatment of disease obviously much stronger sources are needed, and here great care must be exercised to protect patient and doctor. Extensive precautions are taken in the manufacture of radioisotopes at reactors, and in their shipment to medical centers and laboratories.

The radioisotope aspect of neutron capture is useful and fascinating, as we have seen, but there is a further application still more appealing to the imagination. It concerns the information that capture of neutrons can give us, not about the very small, but about the very remote in time—the origin of the elements themselves.

How the Elements Were Formed

Although the origin of the universe and the formation of the elements took place billions of years ago, they are closely related to the matters we have just considered. By observing the ways in which neutrons are captured by nuclei, scientists have discovered an essential clue to the mystery of the formation of the universe—one of the most fundamental problems of physical research.

To explain events that happened so long ago is difficult. Not only are the original occurrences lost in prehistory, but it is a practical impossibility to verify our theoretical conclusions by experiment. The only verification possible in this type of "research" is the evidence still remaining in the present-day universe, together with the assumption that the origin of the universe occurred in accordance with all known physical laws. It was these considerations that led the physicist George Gamow and his colleagues to develop their "neutron-capture theory" of the origin of the elements.

Their starting point was the observed relative abundance of the various chemical elements now existing in the universe. The relative abundance is known not only for the earth but for other parts of the universe as well. Evidence in the more distant regions can be gathered from meteorites hitting the earth from outer space, and from study of the light emitted by distant stars. From these data we know that throughout the universe the light elements, such as hydrogen, helium, and carbon, are much more abundant than the heavier elements, such as lead and gold.

The essential clue to the theory was the fact that the tendency of different nuclei to capture neutrons varies in a manner just the opposite of their abundance. The abundant lightest elements have little tendency to neutron capture, while the less abundant heavier ones capture neutrons eagerly. In fact, if we plot the abundance of elements on a graph, as we do in Figure 25, and then turn this chart upside down, we have what is in all essentials a plot of the neutron-capture affinities of the elements, also given in Figure 25. Evidently there is a close connection between capture of neutrons and the process that long ago gave rise to the elements as we now know them.

Because of this striking correlation, Gamow and his colleagues suggested that several billion years ago the universe consisted simply of a mass of neutrons rapidly traveling outward from a central origin. (The theory does not say what happened at this central point to give rise to the neutrons; the question is reserved for later theorists.) Using this postulate and the known neutron-capture affinities of the elements (those shown in Figure 25), Gamow and his colleagues then computed the ways in which the original free neutrons would combine to form heavier structures. To begin with, of course, these would not resemble the nuclei that now exist—they would contain nothing but neutrons. But any nucleus with an excess of neutrons is radioactive and adjusts itself to stability by converting some of its neutrons to protons, with the emission of radiation. In this way, individual nuclei grew in size by capture of successive neutrons but kept in equilibrium by continued radiation until the great range of nuclei that we know today was formed. This theory has a special appeal. By using only the known properties of nuclei, it is possible to compute the abundance of each element that would finally result—and these computations are in good agreement with what we know to exist.

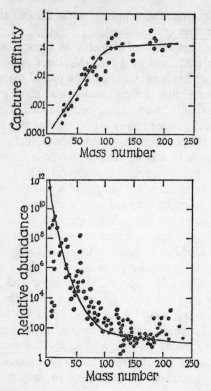

Fig. 25. Affinity for neutron capture of the elements of different mass numbers is the inverse of their abundance in the universe. These charts show the relation. The elements of greatest abundance capture neutrons the least. Scarce elements capture them readily.

This process of element formation, in which new isotopes are made by neutron capture, resembles in many ways the modern production of radioisotopes in a nuclear reactor. Indeed, this theory supposes in effect that the elements were produced in a sort of cosmic nuclear reactor, operating at the fantastically high temperature of about a million degrees, in which tremendous numbers of neutrons were available. And the entire production, according to the theory, was a very rapid one indeed. The expansion of the mass of neutrons and the successive captures giving rise to the familiar elements are assumed to have occurred in only about half an hour!

Obviously, there is no way to check this theory by repeating the growth of elements by neutron capture on a cosmic scale. There are rival theories which hold that the manufacture of elements did not occur once and for all billions of years ago, but that it is continuing still in all galaxies. But, regardless of the specific details, the theory of element formation by neutron capture is a most appealing one, and the close correspondence between known nuclear properties and the observed relative abundance of the elements lends great weight to the probability of its correctness.

Thus the original build-up of matter has provided us with still another example, this time on the cosmic scale, of the clues neutrons give us to the nature of the universe in which we live. Now we shall return to the subatomic scale and consider the properties not of the universe but of the universe in miniature—the nucleus—as revealed by neutrons.

The Cloudy Crystal Ball

As neutrons became available in more and more physics laboratories, and particularly after they could be made in large numbers in nuclear reactors, they were used increasingly for fundamental studies. One method of investigation that gave most surprising results was the use of a beam of neutrons as a probe to study the detailed structure of nuclei. We know that as neutrons move more and more slowly their wave length becomes larger and their chance of interacting with a given nucleus becomes greater. However, we obviously cannot hope to investigate the size and shape of a tiny nucleus by hitting it with a neutron that spreads over regions much larger than the nucleus itself. In order to learn more about the details of nuclear structure, it is necessary to use fast neutrons.

Until a few years ago it was taken for granted that the nucleus was an extremely dense and opaque object, because, as we have seen, it contains in a small space almost the entire mass of the atom. Indeed, when we recall that nuclei are about 1/10,000 as large as atoms, we realize that the density within the nucleus must be about $(10,000)^3$ or 10^{12} (a million million) times greater than the density of ordinary matter. Hence, it was confidently predicted that a fast neutron, with a wave length much smaller than the dimensions of the nucleus, could not possibly pass through a nucleus that it hit, but instead would be absorbed.

Thus it came as a great surprise when it was learned, a few years ago, that neutrons do not inevitably become absorbed when they enter a nucleus—that, in fact, a neutron has a very good chance of passing completely through a nucleus and emerging untouched. Experiments have proved conclusively that in some cases the neutron, behaving as a wave, enters the nucleus and re-emerges, leaving the nuclear particles unchanged. These findings point to the conclusion that, in some way not all understood, the nucleus, despite its enormous density, acts as if it is at least partially transparent to neutron waves.

This surprising behavior of a fast neutron in nuclear matter is not easy to explain in terms of a particle encountering many other particles, but it finds close analogy in the familiar phenomenon of light entering a transparent object, such as a glass block. By utilizing the theory of transmission of light, known for many years, it is possible to predict the behavior of neutrons. In the calculations the neutrons are considered to be refracted in the nucleus according to the laws that are valid for light. As we saw in Chapter 3, the predictions are actually borne out by experimental tests, and the conclusion is thus inescapable that the nucleus must indeed be partially transparent to incoming neutrons. Since *some* of the neutrons are absorbed in passing through the nucleus, it is analogous not to clear glass, but to glass that absorbs some light; that is, "cloudy" glass. This property is usually expressed in the assumption that the nucleus is in a sense a "cloudy crystal ball."

Let us take a moment here to point out that this situation is a good example of the way in which science advances. When we say that the nucleus is "in a sense" a cloudy crystal ball, we are not for a minute implying that the nucleus is made of cloudy glass. Instead we mean that because of some basic similarity the properties of the nucleus resemble closely those of cloudy glass. So we find it fruitful to treat the two situations as if they were the same, and to use the well-understood properties of light for predicting how neutrons will move in the nucleus, of which we have little knowledge. The results obtained correspond surprisingly well to reality, even though, obviously, a nucleus is not glass and neutrons are not light. However, when theory and experiment are examined with great care, it is found that they do not correspond exactly in all details. Nevertheless, such a model of the nucleus is very useful in computing neutron behavior. Since we understand so little of the real nature of the nucleus, it would be impossible to make any predictions at all without making use of some such model. By the very shortcomings of the model when it is compared with more refined experiments, we are enabled to progress to something better—an improved model closer to reality.

At the present time the basic concept of the nucleus as a "cloudy crystal ball" is firmly established, but details of the picture are being carefully modified to reach even better agreement with experiment. For example, one of the present problems is to include in the model the known property that the nucleus is not actually spherical in shape, but slightly egg-shaped. This fact makes the calculation of expected results more complicated, but when they are finally obtained, the predictions of theory are found to agree better with the experimental data.

So we see that the subatomic world possesses yet another strange property, difficult to reconcile with the common-sense concepts of our everyday experience. How can a neutron pass right through a nucleus, in which the density is a million million times greater than that of ordinary matter, without being quickly stopped by the closely packed neutrons and protons? The ultimate reason for the penetrability of the nucleus still escapes us. The present view of physicists is that particles in the nucleus are subject to laws of quantum mechanics that forbid the incoming neutron a place among them. Strange as it may seem, it reacts by passing through as if they did not exist!

Although much remains to be learned about the arrangement of subatomic particles in the nucleus and the laws governing them, progress in this field of research has been remarkable, both in devising models and in uncovering the real nature of the forces that lie behind the typical behavior of the inhabitants of the world of the very small. But neutrons as probes for understanding matter are by no means limited to the nucleus. They are equally potent in studying the behavior of atoms in solids and liquids. Examples of these atomic studies will occupy our next two chapters.

CHAPTER 6

Atomic Patterns

We have now touched on a few of the many ways in which the interactions of neutrons with nuclei have proved to be of great value to many fields of science. They have furnished us information on the nature of the nucleus and the way in which elements were formed billions of years ago. In addition, through the chain reaction, they have made available abundant and varied radioisotopes. For all these things, neutrons are effective because they readily enter nuclei, unhampered by electrical forces. Now we want to look at an entirely new range of problems in which neutrons have been equally productive. Turning away from nuclear structure, we shall examine matter on a scale much larger but still small compared to everyday objects—in other words, let us look at *atoms* and their interactions.

The change in scale is an enormous one. The size of an atom—and its distance to other atoms—is characteristically about ten thousand times greater than the nucleus. And the change is more than one in size alone. The forces that cause atoms to behave toward each other as they do in solids, liquids, and gases are completely different from the forces acting between protons and neutrons in the nucleus. While the nuclear forces are still a major puzzle, connected somehow with mesons, the forces between atoms are the well-known electrical forces exerted between electrons. But in spite of the great difference in magnitude and in the nature of the forces involved, neutrons are as effective in our studies of the relationships of atoms to each other as they are in revealing the nature of the nucleus.

In the use of neutrons to study atomic interactions our principal task is one of determining the configuration or "pattern" of atoms relative to each other and in a wide range of materials, from dense metals to rarefied gases. The study of the patterns of atoms in these materials, and the relationship to physical properties, constitutes the rapidly expanding field called "solid state physics," which, despite its title, deals with atoms in all matter, not merely solids. It is a field of great complexity because matter exists in so many varied forms. It is also of tremendous practical value for its applicability to many branches of industry, from toolmaking to transistors.

Neutrons can be used to study the arrangement and function of atoms in materials by two general methods. In one, materials are bombarded with fast neutrons and the reactions are studied. Atoms are knocked out of their ordinary pattern, and changes in various properties result. Or slow neutrons can be used. Their scatterings reveal the location of atoms within the matter without disturbing them. After a brief explanation of the significance of the fascinating array of atomic patterns, we shall consider a few examples of both methods.

Physical Properties and Atomic Patterns

Astonishing variations in the gross physical properties of matter are caused by the way in which its atoms are arranged. Oxygen gas, for example, (Figure 26) is composed of oxygen atoms arranged in pairs called *molecules,* the members of each pair being tightly bound together by electrical forces but almost completely unaffected by the other oxygen molecules of the gas. Likewise, hydrogen gas consists of molecules, each containing two hydrogen atoms. A mixture of hydrogen and oxygen molecules would be gas, with the molecules affecting each other very little. But if this mixture should be ignited, a chemical reaction would proceed at great speed; hydrogen and

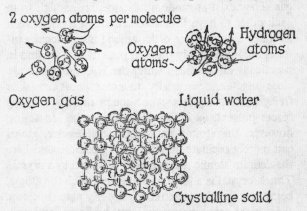

2 oxygen atoms per molecule

Oxygen atoms

Hydrogen atoms

Oxygen gas

Liquid water

Crystalline solid

Fig. 26. Nature's order and disorder are illustrated in the atomic patterns of matter in solid, liquid, and gas forms. The amount of order is least in gases, greatest in crystalline solids.

101

oxygen atoms would combine and form liquid water, consisting of molecules of H_2O.

This great extreme in physical characteristics—invisible gases and liquid water—is determined by the atomic arrangement or *pattern*. The atoms themselves remain essentially unchanged in the formation of water from hydrogen and oxygen. Oxygen gas itself can in fact be converted to a liquid if the temperature is lowered greatly; this liquid oxygen, in appearance very similar to water, differs from the oxygen gas only in that the molecules are closer together and thus exert strong forces on each other. The change of water to ice, and liquid lead to solid lead, are again changes in the atomic patterns, here associated with a decrease in energy so that the electrical forces among the atoms are more effective in holding them together.

There is very little order among the molecules of a gas. They exist at random in space, far enough from each other to have little interaction. In a liquid such as water there is more order among the molecules although not the highly ordered pattern that we find in practically all solids. In water the H_2O molecules are close together, essentially touching, but can slide freely past each other even though there are strong forces present, as indicated in Figure 26. In solids, however, the atomic pattern is very regular, atoms can merely oscillate about a fixed position, and here the definite atomic arrangement is known as a *crystal*. Thus a crystal is a form of matter in which the atoms, being arranged in an extremely orderly pattern, create the typical properties of solidity, hardness, and elasticity.

Even considering solids alone, we find examples of the profound effect of atomic patterns on physical appearance and properties. One of the most striking is the case of diamond and graphite, both consisting of carbon atoms and differing only in the patterns, given in Figure 27, in which they are arranged. The particular pattern existing in diamond is one in which the carbon atoms are held close together, a pattern that unfortunately is very difficult to produce by artificial means. Only recently has it been possible to force the carbon atoms close enough together to produce manmade diamonds, and only small ones at that.

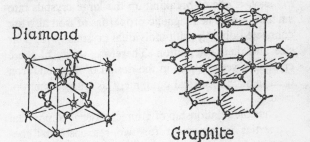

Fig. 27. Diamond and graphite both consist of carbon atoms only but have different atomic patterns. The striking differences in their properties result altogether from this difference in atomic patterns.

In such examples as these the physical properties depending on atomic patterns are obvious to the eye. Many other properties intimately related to patterns are not so obvious but are, nevertheless, of great practical importance. An example is the hardness of a metal: it depends directly on the way in which the atoms are arranged in crystals inside the metal. Careful studies of these patterns and their effects have led to improvements in hardness and resistance to corrosion of metals.

In the usual solids—iron, for instance—the pattern does not persist throughout the piece of iron but actually only in very small regions. In other words, these small regions are individual crystals and the large piece of iron is made up of very many of them. The actual size of the small crystals and their arrangement have a vital effect in determining the physical properties of the iron, its hardness, and electrical and magnetic behavior. A piece of soft iron has large crystals, and the process of hardening iron, by *work hardening,* say, is one of breaking up the large crystals into smaller ones. The magnetic properties of iron also are connected directly with individual crystals—with their size and their orientation. Therefore, study of these crystals is very helpful in the design of magnetic iron used in such electrical equipment as transformers or motors.

Thus the relationship of atomic patterns to physical properties is important for two reasons: first, because it is possible to alter the patterns to produce materials of desired characteristics; second, because investigation of the atomic patterns gives information on the structure of matter, information gained for its own sake rather than for a utilitarian purpose. In many studies it is difficult to distinguish which objective is being followed; the methods are almost the same. Here again, as in most science, we see the intimate relationship between basic research and its applications.

How Fast Neutrons Change Crystals

If we want to alter atomic patterns in order to study the relationship of pattern to physical properties, the most effective tool to produce changes of characteristics in the material is fast neutrons. Slow neutrons, although useful for studying atomic patterns, can do little to alter these patterns. But fast neutrons, as they move through a solid crystalline material, collide with atoms and knock them out of their normal positions. Such displacement of atoms, even though they may be only a tiny fraction of the total number, can alter the basic properties of the crystal, such as its hardness and its ability to transmit heat and electricity. Neutron bombardment produces marked changes in these properties.

A crystal contains such an enormous number of atoms that even if only a very small fraction of them is to be displaced, it is necessary, nevertheless, to use a great many fast neutrons. One of the most efficient ways of getting large numbers of fast neutrons into a material is to place the sample in the center of a nuclear reactor, preferably close to one of the pieces of uranium fuel. The difficulties involved in this technique are severe, for it is necessary to prevent the atoms displaced by the neutrons from returning to their places in the crystal pattern. If the sample is at a high temperature, the atoms move about rapidly and soon find their way back into their original positions. To preserve the neutron-induced changes, it usually is necessary to keep the sample at a very low temperature during and after the neutron irradiation. As the heat production at the center of a nuclear reactor is very great, cooling the sample is not easy, but various ways of doing it have been devised. One method, for instance, is to pump a continuous stream of liquid air through the reactor, so that the intense heat generated in the sample is steadily carried away.

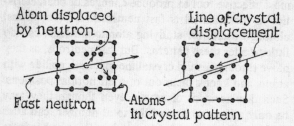

Fig. 28. *Fast neutrons disrupt atomic patterns of crystals, and the effect is compared in this picture with what happens to a metal when it is deformed by "work hardening," the process of pounding or bending it. Neutron bombardment and work hardening produce similar changes in the metal's properties.*

Now that the experimental difficulties have been overcome, scientists have obtained many interesting and valuable results. For example, it has been discovered that a metal actually becomes harder after being subjected to neutron irradiation. This *radiation hardening* is very similar to the familiar *work hardening* produced by any violent mechanical deformation of a metal, such as by forging or hitting it with a heavy hammer. Since neutrons displace only individual atoms, while mechanical deformation causes much larger sections of the metal to be displaced as a whole (Figure 28), it is rather unexpected that the two processes should increase the hardness of a metal by just about the same amount. As we have seen, their rapid motion at high temperatures allows displaced atoms to slip easily back into place. Thus, after the properties of a metal have been altered by neutron bombardment, the metal often can be returned to its original state if it is heated to a high temperature and then slowly cooled. For instance, a radiation-hardened metal, like a work-hardened one, can be softened by heating—a process that is known as *annealing*.

From even these few examples it is clear that investigating the relationship of the crystal structure of a material to its gross physical properties by means of neutron bombardment not only provides us with information of fundamental theoretical importance but is a fruitful source of practical applications as well. The results of experiments like the ones described, for instance, lead us to a better understanding of the complex industrial processes involved in the making of different types of metals. These processes, in many respects more art than science, have been developed over many years by trial-and-error methods, and even today the mechanisms responsible for their success are not fully understood. If neutron-bombardment studies can shed light on the nature of these mechanisms, techniques of producing metals to fit precise specifications can be very much improved.

Neutron Diffraction

In order to study the arrangement of atoms in a crystal without disturbing the atomic pattern, it is necessary to use neutrons that are moving very slowly. Just as determination of the shape of the nucleus required neutrons whose wave length was about the same size, so to investigate atomic patterns it is best to use neutrons whose wave lengths match the distance between atoms. The manner in which such neutrons pass through the atomic pattern is very sensitive to the precise positions of the atoms; hence, they reveal the atomic pattern much better than neutrons of shorter or longer wave length. This method of atomic study could not be seriously considered until the chain reaction had been attained. For it is only with nuclear reactors, in which the chain reaction gives enormous numbers of slow neutrons, that the detailed atomic patterns can be revealed. With the ever-increasing availability of high-powered reactors, this type of investigation has become a most important branch of neutron research. A short time spent in examining the principles of the method is certain to be rewarding to us, for it illustrates so well how the wave properties of neutrons provide a research tool of great power.

The number of very slow neutrons in a nuclear reactor is much larger than those of higher speed. Although we defer until later the simple principles of the chain reaction, at present we can see easily why slow neutrons are so abundant in reactors. The atoms present in all forms of matter are in continual motion, vibrating to and fro, their energy representing the heat energy of the matter. (Even these heat vibrations of atoms are measured with neutrons, as we shall learn in the next chapter.) The neutrons produced in the usual type of reactor decrease in energy when they collide with the atoms in the reactor and finally reach an energy that is the same as these vibrational heat energies, about 0.01 electron volt. On the average, no further loss of energy results, and these slow neutrons accumulate in large numbers in the reactor. The great value of nuclear reactors for neutron diffraction follows from the fortunate fact that these slow neutrons have a wave length, given by the formula of Chapter 3, about the same size as the distance between atoms, which is about 10^{-8} centimeter, less than one hundred-millionth of an inch.

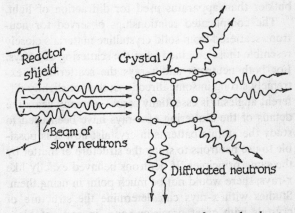

Fig. 29. Neutron diffraction reveals much about crystal structure. The atomic pattern of the crystal can be determined by study of the directions in which the neutrons are scattered.

In the investigation of atomic patterns a beam of slow neutrons impinges on a crystal, as seen in Figure 29, and the directions in which neutrons are scattered from the sample are measured. The number of neutrons scattered varies with the angle in a manner that is extremely complicated: almost none travel in some directions, yet many in others. The neutron waves, which are scattered by all the atoms, add strongly in some directions because of the particular relationship of the atomic locations to the neutron wave length. This addition in specific directions resulting in high intensity is a typical wavelike property, which for ordinary light waves is called *"diffraction."* By analogy, the neutron behavior is called *"neutron diffraction."* Primarily because of the need for extensive shielding, the equipment used for neutron diffraction is much bulkier than apparatus used for diffraction of light.

The complicated relationships observed for neutrons scattered from solid crystalline materials closely resemble those obtained from the scattering of x-rays. For both neutrons and x-rays the scattering is extremely strong in some directions; then at slightly different angles it is essentially zero. For many years the details of the scattering of x-rays have been used to study the atomic patterns in crystals; now it is possible to use neutrons to study the structure of matter by the same principles. If neutrons behaved exactly like x-rays, there would not be much point in using them. Studies with x-rays can determine the structure of crystals with great precision, and, in spite of high-power research reactors, the available intensities of neutrons are still far less than the output of modern x-ray generators. However, neutrons do not scatter in *exactly* the same manner as x-rays, and the differences are of great importance. We shall now look at the two principal applications of neutron diffraction for which x-rays are unsuitable—studies of hydrogen atoms and magnetic atoms.

The Location of Hydrogen Atoms

There are many interesting materials containing hydrogen, and some are of great complexity. But the structures of even the simplest, such as ordinary ice, have been hard to investigate. Most materials not containing hydrogen (salt, which is sodium chloride, for example) have already been well investigated, for example by means of the scattering of x-rays, or x-ray diffraction. The reason for the lack of knowledge about hydrogen is that it contains only one electron per atom, and as a result it does not scatter x-rays effectively. Unlike x-rays, neutrons are scattered by the nucleus of an atom rather than by its electrons, and it does not follow at all that an atom with a small number of electrons will necessarily be a poor scatterer of neutrons. The amount of nuclear scattering depends on many things besides the size of the nucleus alone; mainly it depends on the relationship of the energy of the neutron to the structure of the particular nucleus. In fact, the hydrogen scattering of slow neutrons turns out to be rather large, in spite of the fact that its nucleus consists of but a single proton. Hydrogen scatters neutrons to a much greater extent than helium, though the helium nucleus contains two protons and two neutrons. As a result, it is possible to study the positions of hydrogen atoms with the aid of neutrons, where x-rays would be of practically no avail.

Crystals containing hydrogen form a particularly important group of materials. Among them are numbered not only such familiar substances as ice, but many of the "organic" compounds associated with living tissues. Organic compounds are made up primarily of hydrogen, carbon, and oxygen atoms, arranged into molecules of extreme complexity. Some contain hundreds of atoms. At present we must content ourselves with analyzing only the simplest of these molecules, since the available neutron sources are not intense enough to reveal the structural details of the more complicated ones. As more intense sources become available, it should be possible to study the larger and more complicated molecules with results of the greatest importance to chemistry and biology.

Magnetic Atoms

In addition to the magnitude of scattering by hydrogen atoms, another important difference in the diffraction of neutrons and x-rays arises because neutrons possess magnetic fields. We have considered in Chapter 4 how the magnetic field tells us something about the internal structure of the neutrons; now we are concerned with the use of this field to investigate the magnetic properties of matter. Neutrons are similar to small magnets, and therefore are scattered by the magnetic fields of atoms as well as by their nuclei. This property of magnetic scattering, plus the great ability of neutrons to penetrate solid matter, makes them tools to investigate the detailed nature of magnetic fields far inside pieces of metal. Such studies could not be carried out by older methods, which merely measure the fields outside the objects, since those fields tell us only what is happening on the *average* inside. Further, magnetic investigations are impossible with x-rays; the rays, being an electromagnetic wave motion like visible light, are not scattered by magnetic fields but only by the electrons of atoms. Studies of crystals by x-ray diffraction give the atomic pattern but no information on magnetic structure. Neutron diffraction gives both the atomic positions and the magnetic structure in the same measurement.

Thus neutrons, because of their dual nature as waves and small magnets as well, become effective tools for studying the detailed structure of the atoms and magnetic fields inside such important things as iron. Iron is an example of a *ferromagnetic* metal, which can be magnetized intensely. Its complicated magnetic fields are difficult to investigate by ordinary gross methods, such as measurement of the magnetic fields surrounding a piece of the metal. Such measurements do not reveal the extremely significant information concerning the nature of the magnetic fields around individual iron atoms, but these details now are being investigated by means of neutron diffraction.

Even with neutrons the experiments are by no means simple. In some crystals—for example, the recently discovered *ferrites*—the magnetization of various atoms may be pointing in different directions and

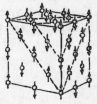

Fig. 30. Pattern of magnetization in a crystal can be measured by neutron diffraction. Because the directions of magnetization for the different atoms are not the same, the crystal shown here is not strongly magnetic as a whole.

possess various strengths. The usual magnetic materials are metals, but ferrites are compounds. They are finding very important applications because they are magnetic but, unlike metals, do not conduct electricity. The complete investigation of such a crystal, as in Figure 30, is a lengthy process, involving measurement of scattered neutrons at many angles for each of many orientations of the crystal, followed by involved analysis of the results. As for the analysis of hydrogen positions, the fascinating study of detailed magnetic structure is just beginning. Results have been of value already in explaining magnetic behavior, and advances in technique will surely prove to be of great theoretical and practical value as well.

Although we have had to move quickly, we have learned to appreciate the relationship between atomic patterns and the more familiar aspects of materials, as hardness and magnetic forces. We have seen also how the patterns can be changed by fast neutrons and investigated by slow neutrons. In all these considerations, we have not concerned ourselves particularly with the fact that the atoms are not stationary in their patterns but are in continual agitated motion. We shall now consider these atomic vibrations in more detail, for here again neutrons are beginning to give much direct information.

CHAPTER 7

Cold Neutrons and Vibrating Atoms

Having seen why slow neutrons are particularly good for investigating crystal atomic patterns, let us now consider a neutron speed even lower, which reveals still other properties of atoms—their actual motions. It is possible, with some difficulty, to obtain neutrons from reactors that have much lower energy than the ones we studied in the last chapter. These, appropriately enough, are called "cold neutrons." They are not used to study the atomic patterns themselves; such use would be impossible, for their wave lengths are much too long to be sensitive to the details of the patterns. Instead, the cold neutrons are of great value in revealing the *motions,* or vibrations, that are exhibited by atoms of all matter.

Atoms of all materials are in rapid, incessant motion—the higher the temperature, the more rapid the motion. We long have had indirect evidence for these motions but now cold neutrons give their details directly. It is because of the slow speed of the cold neutrons that they respond so clearly to the vibrating atoms, which are at much higher temperature. Their speed is affected greatly when they are hit by the moving atoms, and measurement of the change in speed is used to determine the atomic motions accurately. Let us consider briefly how cold neutrons are produced and some of their interesting characteristics, then turn to the way in which they give direct information on the motions of atoms in crystals.

Properties of Cold Neutrons

A few special elements—graphite (carbon) is one—show practically no tendency to absorb neutrons. In graphite a neutron can collide many times with the individual carbon nuclei with little chance of disappearing in the initiation of a nuclear reaction. At each nuclear collision, however, the neutron bounces off, transferring some of its energy of motion to the nucleus and moving more slowly as a result. As we shall see later, a graphite *moderator* is used in many nuclear reactors for this very purpose. If fast neutrons enter a block of graphite, after only a thousandth of a second they will be reduced in energy to that of the graphite atoms, which, of course, are in continuous motion. In this case we can with accuracy speak of the "temperature" of the neutrons, and say that they have been "cooled" to the same temperature as the graphite. The cooling, or moderation, is possible because carbon nuclei have such a low affinity for absorption of neutrons.

When a piece of graphite, or any material, is at a certain temperature, all its atoms are not moving with the same energy. Some are moving faster and some slower than the average velocity, although there are very few with velocities much greater, or much less, than the average. The same type of distribution of velocities holds for the neutrons within the graphite as well, for some of them are moving faster and some slower than the average. We could find some neutrons that by chance are moving *much* more slowly than the average velocity, hence are much "cooler" than the others, but of course they constitute only a small fraction of the total.

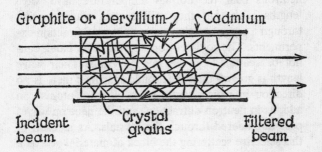

Fig. 31. *"Cold" neutrons, those traveling at low velocity, can be filtered from a beam in an apparatus like this. The crystal grains scatter the fast neutrons, which are absorbed in the cadmium. The slow neutrons pass through.*

The process of producing fast neutrons and slowing them down in graphite is just what happens in the usual type of nuclear reactor. The neutrons result from fission of uranium nuclei, pass into the graphite moderator at high speed, but are soon moderated to the same temperature as the graphite. Among these moderated neutrons, the *fraction* of very slow, or cold neutrons, is small but the total number of neutrons is so enormous that sufficiently many cold neutrons are available for experiments.

Cold neutrons are separated from their warmer

companions in a neutron beam from a reactor. This separation is accomplished by passing the beam through a special material that does not absorb neutrons readily—for example, beryllium, graphite, or lead. One of these materials, if in the form of small crystals, as shown in Figure 31, will allow only the very cold neutrons to pass through it. As we have learned, neutrons near the normal temperature have wave lengths such that they will scatter when passing through a crystal, as they do in neutron diffraction experiments. The cold neutrons, on the other hand, cannot be scattered by the small crystals. Their wave length is greater than the atomic spacings; there is no direction in which waves from different atoms can add, as in neutron diffraction, and the neutron waves pass unhindered through the crystals. As a result of this selective scattering the block of material acts as a *neutron filter:* the cold neutrons pass through it freely, but the faster neutrons are scattered by the crystal grains and captured in the surrounding layer of cadmium, a strong absorber.

One material that has been used as a filter for production of cold neutrons is graphite itself; another is the metal beryllium, which furnishes a more intense beam than graphite. When neutrons are passed through a beryllium filter, the emergent beam is cold, indeed, with a temperature much below the surroundings. Specifically, the temperature is about 35 degrees on the "absolute scale," or 35 degrees above absolute zero. As this is a temperature of 238 degrees below zero centigrade or 396 degrees below zero Fahrenheit, there is no doubt that the filtering in beryllium does "cool" neutrons! On an atomic scale, neutrons of this extremely low temperature move slowly, although their velocity, of course, is still high compared with ordinary objects. The speed of the neutrons filtered through beryllium is about 750 meters per second, or 1700 miles per hour! Yet on a subatomic scale the neutrons are really moving very slowly, for most par-

Neutrons of many velocities

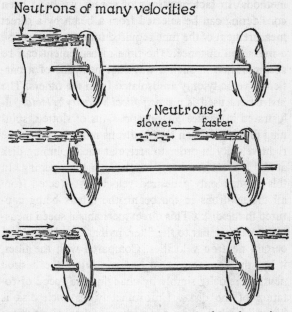

Neutrons
slower ————→ faster

Fig. 32. Neutron "chopper," shown in this schematic representation, is a mechanical velocity selector that allows only neutrons of one velocity to pass through its slots. The speed of rotation of the discs is the controlling factor. In operation, incident neutrons cover the whole disc. What comes out is not a single bundle of neutrons but a screw-shaped beam of neutrons of the same velocity. Usually the instrument has several discs to improve the precision of velocity selection.

119

ticles produced in nuclear reactions are about a thousand times faster.

But even on the scale of normal objects, the cold neutrons are not moving too rapidly for their velocity to be measured by direct, relatively simple mechanical methods. In fact, neutrons of speeds we have been considering can be selected from a beam by a direct measurement of the time required for them to traverse a measured distance. The time measurement can be accomplished in such a way that neutrons of a particular velocity only are isolated from the others. The instrument used is a *mechanical velocity selector,* illustrated in Figure 32, an apparatus of slotted, spinning disks. It is seen that neutrons must have just the right velocity in order to arrive at each spinning disk at the correct time to pass through the opening. In this manner only a desired velocity is selected from all the neutrons in the beam, the others being captured in the disks. This direct mechanical speed measurement is similar to the filter, in that they both select certain neutron velocities. Compared with the filter, it has the advantage that one can select the desired neutron velocity simply by changing the speed of rotation of the disks. Unfortunately, as each disk is "open" such a short time, the number of neutrons obtained is very low.

Both methods of obtaining cold neutrons, the filter and the mechanical velocity selector, have been of great use in the study of motions of atoms. The slowly moving neutrons, penetrating into the object under study, are affected profoundly by collisions with the atoms, thus revealing clearly the detailed atomic motions. But before we look at these interesting and revealing experiments, let us consider a few of the simplest properties of moving atoms.

Atomic Vibrations as Heat Energy

It has been known for a long time that heat is simply one of the many forms in which energy exists, and that the quantity of heat energy possessed by an object is directly shown by its temperature. When heat is added to a block of iron, for example, its temperature rises; when twice the amount of heat is added, there is twice the temperature rise, provided the block does not melt. If we could look at the individual atoms in the iron block with some kind of super-microscope, we would see that they are in constant motion to and fro. We also would see that after heat energy is added to the iron they move more rapidly. The higher the temperature, the faster the iron atoms move, each vibrating about its average position in the atomic pattern of the iron crystal. The temperature of the block of iron is proportional to the average energy of vibration; some atoms have more, some less, than this average energy.

When we consider the details of the atomic motion in crystals, we find them interesting both in relation to temperature and because of the facts they reveal concerning why atoms form crystal patterns. There are electrical forces between the atoms, and the forces hold them in their regular pattern as the crystal is formed. As a result, the motion of one atom is by no means independent of those of other nearby atoms within the crystal; in fact, the details of the motions give direct information about the forces among the atoms. Should one atom be disturbed and set into motion, it causes the next atom to move by means of the force they exert on each other. The second atom in turn moves a third, and so on. In this way motion is communicated through the crystal just as waves are propagated through water. Indeed, the spread of the disturbance throughout the crystal *is* a wave.

The type of wave carried through the crystal by the vibrating atoms is a "sound" wave, although usually of much too high a pitch to be audible. Sound waves of an enormous range in pitch, or *frequency,* are found in crystals, from the very low frequencies that are audible sound to frequencies billions of times greater. The highest frequencies to which our ears are sensitive range up to about ten thousand vibrations per second. Vibrations can exist in crystals with frequencies up to 10^{13}, or 10^9 times greater than the highest frequencies of the audible range. The physical laws governing their behavior are the same, in spite of this billionfold difference in frequency.

The details of the motions set up in crystals when heat energy is added to them eluded experimental observation for many decades. Even worse, the relationship between the heat energy added and the observed rise in temperature could not be explained by assuming any system of vibrations at all! It was this very problem that provided the principal clue leading to the discovery of *quantum mechanics* in 1900. Atoms in gaining heat energy did not act as if they were simple mechanical bodies held together by well-known electrical forces, free to take on energy in any available amounts. Instead, the energy was added in a way not familiar with large-scale objects, for it was transferred only in definite amounts, never continuously. The peculiarities of the process led the German physicist Planck to the realization that the energy, as we said in Chapter 3, existed in discrete amounts, each a *quantum* of energy.

Detailed theoretical calculations of atomic vibrations have been made, based on quantum mechanics. Until recently there was no direct way of observing the vibrations to see if they correspond with the predictions of quantum mechanics. Of course, the *average* energy of the vibrations can be obtained easily from the measured temperature rise associated with addition of definite amounts of heat, for the temperature is a direct measure of the average energy of motion. But these measurements do not give any information about the details of the vibrations such as the number of vibrations of different frequencies; that is, the *frequency distribution*. With the availability of slow neutrons from reactors, however, it has become possible to observe the motions so directly that we can almost "see" the vibrations over the entire frequency range. These experiments, which we shall now describe, are a dramatic illustration of the ability of neutrons to get within materials and reveal intimate details of the structure and the motion of the constituent atoms.

How Cold Neutrons Reveal Atomic Motions

Cold neutrons, as we have said, are useful for studying moving atoms within crystals partly because they penetrate most solid material so readily. More importantly, however, collisions with the moving atoms cause changes in energy much larger than the neutrons initially have. These advantages are related;

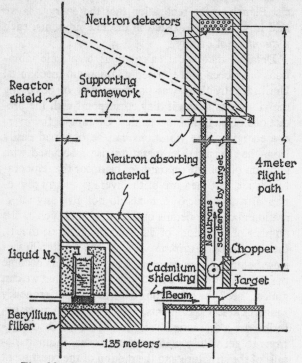

Fig. 33. Atomic vibrations are measured with cold neutrons in the apparatus schematically pictured here. Liquid nitrogen (temperature about −200°C) cools the filter for increased production of the cold neutrons. After scattering in the sample being studied, the neutrons go through chopper to detector for velocity measurements.

the "coldness" of the neutron is what causes the great penetrating power because it implies a wave length too large to be scattered in the crystal by the usual process of neutron diffraction. The scattering of the cold neutrons that does occur is a different process, in which the moving atom hits the very slow neutron and knocks it out of the crystal. While rare, this scattering with large energy gain is our primary concern right now. The scattered neutrons leave the crystal moving much faster than they enter. Measurement of the velocities of the emerging neutrons enables us to gain very directly a picture of the energies or motions of the atoms in the crystal.

In Figure 33 we see an outline of the method by which cold neutrons are produced and used to study the atomic motions. Emerging from a hole in the shield of a nuclear reactor is a beam of neutrons with a temperature about that of ordinary matter, for they have come from the graphite moderator of the reactor. They pass through a filter, here beryllium, which we know allows only the very cold neutrons to pass toward the sample of material being studied.

The moving atoms of the sample will scatter a few of the neutrons that pass through it, giving these neutrons amounts of energy much larger than they possessed on entering. As the purpose of the experiment is to obtain the energy of these scattered neutrons, equipment is arranged to measure their velocity. For this purpose, scattered neutrons moving in a selected direction (those scattered by 90 degrees in this experiment) pass through the opening in a shutter. The shutter is open only a few millionths of a second. The time between the closing of the shutter and the arrival of the neutron at the detector is measured by electronic circuits. Thus, the time required for the neutrons to traverse the distance from the shutter to the detector gives the velocity, hence the energy, of the scattered neutrons. The shutter is actually a rapidly rotating cylinder, containing slots that allow neutrons to pass through as it spins. For obvious reasons it is usually called a neutron "chopper."

It is found that for most materials at ordinary temperature the energy of the scattered neutrons—that is, their temperature—corresponds roughly to the temperature of the scattering sample. Thus the neutron beam is actually "heated" from 238 degrees C. below zero, the cold neutron temperature, to about 20 degrees C. above, a gain of 258 degrees C. by only one scattering per neutron!

Although the energy given to the scattered neutrons is directly related to the energy of the atomic vibration, it is a complex matter to analyze the experimental results in general and obtain the detailed motions of the vibrating atoms. Fortunately, however, some crystals are particularly easy to analyze. As the entire technique has been developed only recently, it has been used so far primarily for the simpler materials. In order to show the power of this new method in revealing atomic motions, we shall describe briefly the results for two particularly simple materials, the metal vanadium and zirconium hydride, a material containing hydrogen.

The Distribution of Vibration Frequencies

Measurements of atomic vibrations with cold neutrons are rather complicated for most crystals because neutrons of such low energy show wave properties so strongly. We are inaccurate when we think of a neutron's being hit by a single atom alone as if it were a small particle. Because such slow neutrons are really widely extended waves, they interact with nuclei of many atoms of the crystal at the same time, and in the scattering the effects of all these add. The individual waves interfere with one another, just as ripples do on the surface of a pond, and the resulting pattern of scattered neutrons is complex indeed. Although this complexity holds for most crystals, there are a few, particularly vanadium and hydrogen, in which the scattering is far simpler.

This simplicity of neutron scattering in vanadium and hydrogen arises from the unusual fact that the neutron wave scattered by each atom of these two elements is completely independent of the scattering from all others. The independence of the scattering is involved in the particular nuclear structure of vanadium and hydrogen, and although we cannot examine the details here, the result is easy to state. When a neutron scatters from a vanadium nucleus, for example, it interacts with that nucleus alone, with no regard for nuclei of neighboring atoms. As a result, the scattering pattern is simple and the energy of the scattered neutrons tells us exactly what energies are possessed by the vibrating vanadium atoms in the crystal.

Because of this simplicity of cold-neutron scattering by vanadium, it is an excellent material for checking the theoretical predictions of the kinds of motions that are present in all crystals. For many years it had been assumed that the distribution of energies, or frequencies, of the vibrations is a particularly simple one, although direct measurements were impossible. This theory assumed a distribution of more and more vibrations as the frequency, which is proportional to energy, increased up to a certain maximum frequency.

Above the maximum the intensity, or number of vibrations, would drop abruptly to zero. Recently it has been possible to check the theory directly. The number of vibrations of different frequencies present within the crystal has been measured for vanadium metal by means of cold neutrons.

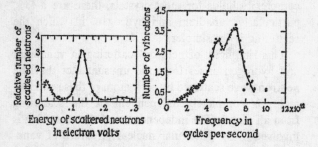

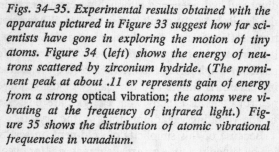

Figs. 34–35. Experimental results obtained with the apparatus pictured in Figure 33 suggest how far scientists have gone in exploring the motion of tiny atoms. Figure 34 (left) shows the energy of neutrons scattered by zirconium hydride. (The prominent peak at about .11 ev represents gain of energy from a strong optical vibration; the atoms were vibrating at the frequency of infrared light.) Figure 35 shows the distribution of atomic vibrational frequencies in vanadium.

The results of the measurement of the distribution of frequencies—ranging up to the highest frequencies found, about 10^{13} vibrations per second—are shown in Figure 35. These show that the general shape of the distribution at low frequencies—that is, frequencies of ordinary sound—is similar to the simple theoretical curve. However, the most significant results are those at very high frequencies, billions of cycles per second, where it is seen that instead of the smooth curve predicted by the theory, there are actually peaks and valleys present.

The reason for the failure of the theory at high frequencies is that it is based on a picture, or model, of the crystal that is much too simple. The model does not include the variations in the crystal from atom to atom, variations that are of importance only for short wave length; that is, high-frequency vibrations. The measured results tell us that in the crystal things are much more complicated than is assumed in the simple theory, and these results enable us to learn how the real crystal differs from the theoretical model. Very recent theoretical calculations, taking into account the detailed atomic pattern and the differing forces between various atoms, have shown that peaks of the type shown in the figure actually should be present. But the theoretical calculation is a lengthy, difficult one, and no exact result for vanadium is available yet. Here the exact results of the measurement are easier to obtain than the calculated results of the theory, but both are necessary to understand the forces between the atoms of the crystal.

Optical Vibrations of Hydrogen

As many important materials contain hydrogen, it is indeed fortunate that the scattering of cold neutrons from hydrogen has the same simplicity as from vanadium, and that the experimental results are correspondingly easy (if "easy" is the word) to analyze. Thus, in considering the scattering of cold neutrons from materials containing hydrogen, we do not need to take into account complicated interference of

129

waves. The energy of the scattered neutrons gives us, just as it does for vanadium, a direct picture of the atomic motions.

Of course, one obvious difference between crystals containing hydrogen and the element vanadium is that for the former there are several kinds of atoms in the crystal. As a result, a type of motion becomes possible that cannot take place in a simple crystal, such as vanadium, containing only one type of atom. This kind of motion is a vibration in which two different kinds of atoms vibrate relative to each other, with their average position remaining almost stationary. These vibrations are really not sound waves at all but more closely resemble the kind of motion that would be aroused in a crystal when light is absorbed by it. The frequency is extremely high: 10^{13} per second, or ten million megacycles, which is the frequency of infrared light, instead of sound. These vibrations are commonly called *optical vibrations,* to distinguish them from the type we have considered already, which are called *acoustic vibrations.* The acoustic vibrations are of lower frequency, and for very low frequencies, below 10^4 per second, are ordinary sound waves.

The optical frequencies can be studied with cold neutrons in exactly the manner we have just described for acoustic vibrations. A particular crystal containing hydrogen, zirconium hydride, was the first to be used for detection of optical vibrations with cold neutrons. This material is used in one type of nuclear reactor to reduce the speed of fast neutrons; that is, as a "moderator." In this application, the way in which energy is transferred *from* neutrons *to* the atoms of zirconium and hydrogen is of great importance for safe operation of the nuclear reactor. When the scattering has reduced the neutrons almost to the temperature of the moderator, then the details of the atomic vibrations, particularly the high-frequency optical ones, are most important.

Cold neutron experiments with zirconium hydride tell us what energies are gained *from* the atomic vibrations by the neutrons, whereas in the reactor the reverse process occurs: neutrons transfer energy *to* the vibrations. Nevertheless, the cold-neutron results furnish exactly the desired information, for the atomic vibrations give to the cold neutrons exactly the same energies that they would receive from faster neutrons in a nuclear reactor. The measured energies of cold neutrons scattered from zirconium hydride are of great interest because they exhibit an extremely prominent peak, shown in Figure 34. The vibration frequency necessary to give rise to this peak is high, and the vibration is thus definitely an optical one. The energy of the neutrons in this peak corresponds to a temperature of 1300 degrees C., which, of course, is well above that of the moderator of a reactor. Thus, for a zirconium-hydride moderator there is an extremely high probability that neutrons, slowing down in collisions, will suddenly give energy *to* the atoms, exciting the optical vibration, as they reach this temperature. Obviously this absorption of energy could have a strong effect on the operation of the reactor—in this case it helps to make it more stable.

The experiments with cold neutrons that we have been reviewing show again the power of neutrons in penetrating matter and revealing phenomena hitherto difficult or impossible to study. Although we have considered only two examples, they illustrate well how the results give much basic information concern-

131

ing the forces between atoms in crystals, and as well have practical results of great importance. But we must cut short our brief visit to the field of atomic patterns and motions and end our story with the major practical triumph of the neutron—the achievement of the nuclear chain reaction.

CHAPTER 8

The Chain Reaction

At the beginning of our story we saw how in its short lifetime the neutron has attained world importance. The neutron was only thirteen years of age when the atomic bomb drew the world's attention to its potency. This immense release of nuclear energy, the production of electrical power, the wide availability of radioisotopes, and motive power for ships—all these are important practical results of the nuclear chain reaction, made possible by neutrons.

The chain reaction is a process releasing nuclear energy; once started, it can increase enormously in power. The reaction is based on a very special type of nuclear transformation possible only in very heavy nuclei, the process known as *fission*. It is only because neutrons can cause fission in heavy nuclei that the chain reaction and its great range of applications—electrical power, motive power and bombs—are possible. Very recently, another type of chain reaction, based on *fusion* of light nuclei, has been given increasing attention, but almost all the enormous activity throughout the world in atomic energy at the present time is based on fission. Let us look briefly at this unusual nuclear reaction, then at the way in which chain reactions, bombs, and nuclear reactors operate, and finally at the possibility for fusion reactions. While it is not our purpose in the story of the neutron to devote much space to engineering matters, no story of the neutron would be complete without a brief glimpse of the ways in which this small particle is destined to affect the lives of us all on the practical level.

Fission Fundamentals

Ever since Einstein showed that mass was equivalent to energy, scientists had been aware of the possibility that matter itself might serve as a potent source of energy. The only known examples of the conversion, however, were nuclear reactions in which a very small number of nuclei would change into others, losing mass that would appear as energy. As we know, it became much easier to produce nuclear reactions when slow neutrons became available. Even then the number of nuclei that would react in a material subjected to neutron bombardment was still much too small to produce practical amounts of energy. A few years after the neutron's discovery many scientists were studying the nuclear changes induced by neutrons, but primarily to learn about the structure of the nucleus. None seriously considered the possibility that sizable amounts of matter might be caused to disappear, resulting in the release of large amounts of energy. The reason for their pessimism was that there was no known way in which a nuclear transformation would propagate itself through the material, no way in which the transformation of one nucleus would cause other nuclei to change too.

Indeed, the process that ultimately made the propagation possible—*fission*—was completely unexpected when discovered. In 1938 two German scientists, Otto Hahn and F. Strassmann, were bombarding a variety of elements with neutrons, just as many other scientists were doing throughout the world. They discovered that while most nuclei changed only slightly after absorbing a neutron, the uranium nucleus changed by a large amount. As depicted in Figure 36, it actually split in two. Further, the combined weight of the parts into which the uranium nucleus split was less than the weight of the original uranium nucleus. And, as must follow from Einstein's equation, this decrease in mass appeared as—or rather was converted into—energy. The energy is present in the form of motion, or *kinetic energy,* of the fragments of the uranium nucleus, which separate at tremendous speed.

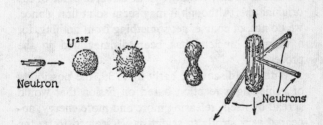

Fig. 36. Fission of U^{235} can be thought of as occurring in steps: first, absorption of a neutron in the nucleus; second, the agitated nucleus, with the extra neutron; third, the beginning of fission; finally, fission with the emission of two or three neutrons.

135

So far this process of fission, surprising as it is, differs from an ordinary nuclear reaction primarily in that the amount of energy released is much larger, actually about a hundredfold greater, than is usually produced in a nuclear reaction. Still another property that was found, soon after the initial discovery of fission, made it unique among nuclear reactions. As the uranium nucleus split, not only was energy released, but in the process several additional neutrons (Figure 36) were emitted. Actually, when we consider the structure of the nucleus, the emission of neutrons is not surprising. The uranium nucleus contains very many neutrons, and the energy released in the fission causes neutrons to be "boiled off" the fragments as they fly apart.

The emission of neutrons, along with energy, during the act of fission completely changed the prospects for release of nuclear energy on a practical, useful scale. For in fission we start with one neutron and end with the release of a large amount of energy plus several neutrons, usually two or three, in place of the original one. Although it may seem so at first glance, we do not, of course, get something from nothing, for a uranium nucleus has been disintegrated in the process.

With this discovery, early in 1939, the possibility of achieving a reaction based on fission that would spread by itself, releasing more and more energy, appeared very strong to scientists. It seemed to be the perfect answer in the search for a method of releasing the enormous stores of energy held in nuclei in the form of mass.

The Nuclear Chain Reaction

It should be clear to us now, as it was to all nuclear scientists in 1939, why it is that fission could produce a reaction that would sustain itself—in other words, a nuclear *chain reaction*. If the neutrons emitted during the fission of one uranium nucleus can be made to cause other uranium nuclei to split, still more neutrons would be produced, which could be used to tap the energy of still more nuclei. Assuming that a fissioning uranium nucleus emits three neutrons and that each of these enters another uranium nucleus, we then would have nine neutrons after these nuclei have split. After another repetition of the process we would have 3 x 3 x 3 or 27 neutrons, then 81 neutrons, then 243, 729, and so on.

This process of successive multiplications by three leads to enormous numbers very quickly; at the thirteenth step we have produced more than one million neutrons! Moreover, the time required for the process is incredibly short, for the neutrons produced in fission move at high speed, about eight thousand miles per second, and the nuclei are close together. In fact, the time elapsing between release of a neutron during fission of one nucleus and its splitting of another is only one billionth of a second. Thus, if the process should proceed as we describe it, the neutrons would be multiplied threefold every billionth of a second— an awesome process. But the "if" that we have just included is very important. It is by no means certain that the three neutrons produced in the fission of uranium will cause three other uranium nuclei to split. The difficulty arises from a nuclear fact with which we are familiar already—a neutron penetrates extremely easily through matter, having small chance indeed of scoring a direct hit on a nucleus. And only if the neutron collides directly with the nucleus of the uranium atom can it cause fission and production of more neutrons.

To visualize the problem more vividly, let us imagine an experiment in which we are shooting neutrons at a small piece of uranium, say the size of a marble. Here we easily realize that a chain reaction simply cannot take place. Now and then a neutron will split a uranium nucleus, but the neutrons thereby produced will almost certainly pass out of the small piece of uranium and nothing further will happen. In other words, our successive multiplication, $3 \times 3 \times 3$ . . . , will not occur and there will be no chain reaction. It is easy to conclude what we must do, *in principle,* to attain success—increase the size of the lump! However, it is impossible to say, without a great deal of additional information, how large the lump must be in order to keep neutrons from escaping and thus attain a chain reaction. It might even be possible that the chain reaction would not occur however much the lump of uranium should be enlarged.

Soon after the discovery of fission, experiments showed that it was the isotope U^{235} that split, not the much more abundant U^{238}. As a result, as was soon learned, the chain reaction could never be attained in a lump of normal uranium metal, regardless of size. For the pure U^{235} isotope, measurements revealed that the chain reaction would be attained if the lump should be larger than a certain *"critical size,"* several inches in diameter. An amount of U^{235} less than critical will not support the chain reaction (see Figure

37) and is a harmless, nonexplosive piece of metal. But once the lump is increased beyond the critical size, things are far different. Should a fission occur, the resulting neutrons will not escape, and their number as well as the rate of energy release will increase rapidly. If the U^{235} should be well over the critical amount, an explosion of tremendous violence would result.

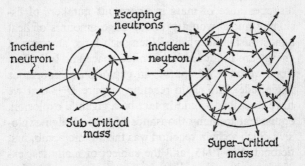

Fig. 37. Sub- and super-critical masses of uranium behave differently after absorption of a neutron. The process is shown schematically here. Many more collisions occur in the super-critical lump.

Now we are in a position to examine briefly how the chain reaction is applied in the atomic bomb and, in a controlled way, in the nuclear reactor. The outward results of these two types of release of nuclear energy are far different, yet in both the products of the chain reaction are the same. They are (1) energy, which results from the conversion of mass and appears as energy of motion of the fission fragments, (2) fission fragments, usually very unstable and hence intensely radioactive, and (3) neutrons, emitted copiously in all chain reactions.

The Atomic Bomb

The fission chain reaction, under the ideal conditions we have pictured, would proceed with extraordinary speed; the process of multiplication by three repeating a thousandfold before even a millionth of a second had elapsed. The release of energy from the disappearance of mass in enormous numbers of fissioning nuclei would produce large amounts of heat almost instantaneously. When such large amounts of energy are produced in a limited space and in a short time, we have, of course, an explosion of enormous magnitude. The chain reaction in pure U^{235} that we have described would in fact be a gigantic explosion, equivalent to many thousands of tons of high explosive. Such a chain reaction was the atomic bomb, first detonated in 1945, and the subject of many test explosions since then.

An amount of U^{235} definitely larger than the critical size will inevitably and immediately explode violently if quickly assembled into a compact mass. There is no need to start the chain reaction by bombarding the assembled supercritical mass with neutrons. There are many neutrons constantly present through the earth's atmosphere, produced by *cosmic rays,* which are high-energy protons entering the atmosphere from outer space. In addition, some of the uranium nuclei undergo *spontaneous fission,* without the help of incident neutrons, and, of course, produce neutrons by so doing. As a result, there always are some neutrons present in uranium so that the chain reaction will proceed immediately once the assembled mass becomes supercritical.

If we now consider the practical problem of actual assembly of a supercritical mass of U^{235}, we immediately realize the serious difficulties to be surmounted. As soon as the amount should exceed the critical by even the slightest margin, the chain reaction would start. But, as many of the neutrons still would escape, the intensity would increase much more slowly than we have depicted in our ideal situation. Eventually sufficient heat would be developed to melt and disperse the uranium; the reaction would then stop before an explosion had been developed. Thus we see that the problem of detonating an atomic bomb —that is, of creating a high-efficiency explosion—is one of getting more than the critical amount of fissionable material into a compact mass *before* a low-intensity chain reaction itself disintegrates the mass of material.

The process of attaining the rapid assembly of the bomb material is by no means a simple one. In order to get an atomic-bomb explosion of reasonable efficiency, one in which a large fraction of the contained uranium undergoes fission, it is necessary to assemble the parts of the supercritical mass with almost unbelievable speed. This phase of the operation is a matter of first-class engineering, not nuclear physics; it is actually accomplished with high explosives. These are arranged in such a way that the U^{235}, which has been separated into small amounts and hence is subcritical, is suddenly slammed together so that the supercritical mass is obtained. The explosion is made even more efficient by surrounding the components with a heavy metal container, which helps hold the U^{235} together until as many as possible of the uranium nuclei have released their fission energy.

So far the sole application of atomic bombs has been in warfare, and this severely limited function is usually considered to be the only one that they possess. But the possibility has arisen recently of peacetime uses of atomic bombs. They of course must be limited to those particular circumstances in which the explosive release of large amounts of energy would be of great value and the radioactivity produced would not be dangerous. It may be possible that bombs, especially those augmented with fusion power, the process to be described later, can be arranged so that the radioactivity produced creates no danger. These explosions might find uses in construction projects in which large amounts of earth must be moved, such as the formation of harbors and canals. It is also possible that atomic bombs could be used to reactivate oil wells that have ceased to produce by violently modifying the rock structure in the surroundings. Little is known at the present time as to whether such beneficial uses of atomic-bomb explosions will be possible, economically feasible, and safe, but scientists are considering them seriously. Several test atomic explosions have been detonated underground already, the largest equivalent to twenty thousand tons of TNT, and the radioactivity produced has been successfully contained.

The Nuclear Reactor

Let us turn now to the principal peacetime way in which the neutron has grown to international importance. This accomplishment is the production of atomic power, with its manifold applications, by means of the controlled chain reaction. The chain reaction that we have considered thus far is a most explosive one—it can hardly be called controlled. Somewhat surprisingly perhaps, it is easier to release atomic energy in chain reactions at a slow, controlled rate than to make a bomb. In fact, the first chain reaction was not the atomic bomb but a low-power controlled reaction, obtained in 1942, three years before the first atomic explosion. The main reason for the earlier attainment of the controlled chain reaction is that it is not necessary to use the single isotopes U^{235}, as in the bomb, but simply the element as it occurs in nature—about 99 per cent U^{238} and 1 per cent U^{235}.

The work leading up to that first chain reaction in 1942 was done at the University of Chicago, under the direction of Enrico Fermi, the eminent physicist whose fundamental experiments in neutron physics we previously considered. The reaction took place in what is now called a nuclear reactor, then known as a chain-reacting *"pile"*—a very suitable name, since the reactor consisted merely of a pile of graphite blocks interspersed with lumps of uranium. Graphite was chosen for the pile material because carbon atoms of which it is composed do a very efficient job of slowing down neutrons, but have a relatively small tendency to absorb them. Thus the presence of graphite ensures that a large percentage of the neutrons produced in the fission of uranium will themselves go on to produce other fissions. The pile, like the components of an atomic bomb, had a critical size, but its critical size, instead of a few inches, was fifteen feet.

When the pile was made larger than critical, it began to chain react, but did not explode. The reason is that, just as for pure U^{235}, the chain reaction increases in intensity extremely slowly if the amount of material is barely above critical. The structure was built with great care to assure just such a slowly increasing reaction rate. It was found to be very easy to control the rate of the chain reaction, or power of the pile, by simply inserting a cadmium rod into the pile to regulate it. Cadmium is such a strong neutron absorber that, upon insertion, it would stop the chain reaction completely. The pile power could be held at any desired level by simple motions of the cadmium rod, called the "control rod."

Although the low-power chain reaction was easy to produce, once pure uranium and graphite were available, a long road yet remains before there is widespread and practical production of electric power from nuclear reactors. The power produced in the first chain-reacting pile appeared as heat; the graphite and uranium of the pile became hotter as the chain reaction continued. But in order to get useful power, say as electricity, from the chain reaction, the great quantities of heat energy must be removed and transformed into electrical energy. Present-day reactors are far different from Fermi's simple pile.

Having been studied and developed over many years, the process of converting heat energy into steam, then into electrical energy in a turbine, is highly advanced. But in converting the heat of nuclear fission there are many problems in addition to those arising in the production of electricity by the burning of coal.

In any chain reaction, as we have seen, one of the products is the radioactive fission fragments. Thus inevitably in any atomic power plant large amounts of radioisotopes, with enormous radiation intensity, will be produced. The problems associated with the safe handling of this radioactivity are new and formidable problems in the generation of electrical power on a broad and inexpensive scale. When heat is produced in a nuclear reactor, the radioactivity is so intense that it is all but impossible to repair equipment. Because of the great hazard of radioactivity it is necessary, although difficult and expensive, to design a plant that will not need repairs for years.

At the present time electrical power is being produced from nuclear energy in a few plants, and many more are now being built throughout the world. But because of the problems inherent in the dangers of radioactivity, atomic power is still more expensive, unfortunately, than power produced from the burning of coal or water power. In time coal will rise in price as supplies are exhausted, and atomic heat, as we gain experience, will become cheaper. So it seems inevitable that atomic power will someday compete economically with coal and water power. The precise time—estimates vary from three to ten years—will depend on a variety of local conditions, but the ultimate outcome seems certain. Nuclear energy is destined to become the primary source of the world's power supply.

Fusion—The Power of the Future?

We now come to the end of our story of the neutron and conclude with a subject that looks to the future—a new type of chain reaction that holds great promise but presents even more formidable difficulties than fission. It is a chain reaction based on the nuclear process of *fusion,* which proceeds oppositely to fission. While the net result is the same as fission

—the release of nuclear energy on a large scale—fusion is the joining of light nuclei rather than the disruption of heavy nuclei. The neutron, although playing an important role, is not an essential key to the attainment of the fusion chain reaction as it is for fission. In fact, that very circumstance is the primary obstacle in the development of a practical fusion reaction.

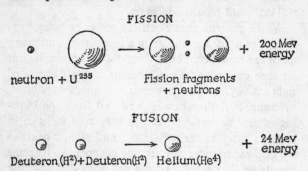

$$\text{FISSION}$$

neutron + U^{235} Fission fragments + neutrons   + 200 Mev energy

$$\text{FUSION}$$

Deuteron (H^2) + Deuteron (H^2)   Helium (He^4)   + 24 Mev energy

Fig. 38. Fission and fusion both release energy, as indicated in this sketch, but in a sense they proceed oppositely.

The fission chain reaction takes place readily because uncharged neutrons can penetrate unhindered to the nuclei of the uranium atoms. In contrast, the process of fusion is one in which very light positively charged *nuclei,* such as hydrogen and lithium, combine to release energy, an enormously more difficult process. The elementary facts of both processes are compared in Figure 38. The great obstacle in the path to fusion arises because the light nuclei, unlike neutrons, are electrically charged, and the repulsion makes it very difficult to get them to join together, or to fuse. The only way to cause nuclei to fuse is to set them into rapid motion so that two can touch in spite of the repulsive electrical force. And to get the atoms of a material into rapid motion means raising them to an extremely high temperature—to many millions of degrees, in fact. Only at such an enormous temperature are the nuclei moving fast enough to combine and release energy by fusion.

Of course, once an appreciable number of nuclei fuse, thereby emitting energy, the temperature will rise even higher, the nuclei will fuse more rapidly, and we have the essential conditions for the propagation of a chain reaction. In these nuclear reactions of fusion energetic neutrons are produced, which, by causing further nuclear reactions, help to raise the temperature even more. Thus, while neutrons are produced in the reaction and increase its intensity, they do not play the crucial role that they do for fission.

The technical problem of producing fusion power on a large scale is one of attaining high temperature in a gas composed of light atoms, principally hydrogen. This reaction is called a *thermonuclear* reaction because it is a nuclear reaction caused by heat, or "thermal" energy. No ordinary container like steel, glass, or concrete could withstand the necessary temperatures, well over a million degrees; hence it is necessary to hold the incredibly hot light atoms by some other method. At the present stage of thermonuclear research, essentially all the effort is directed toward use of magnetic fields to keep the hot atoms in a confined space.

At high temperature, electrons are stripped from the hydrogen atoms by incessant collision with other atoms; hence, the light atoms are positively charged and their motions are strongly affected by the mag-

147

netic fields. Such a gas of hot atoms with their electrons removed is called a *plasma*. With properly placed magnetic fields to cause the charged atoms to move in sharply curved paths it is conceivable that they might remain in a limited volume, even though moving rapidly because of their high temperature. The device shown in Figure 39 is an example of one present approach to the problem of holding or "containing" a hot plasma.

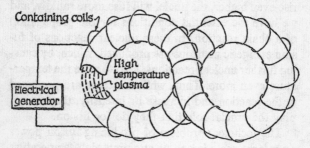

Fig. 39. Thermonuclear power is the goal of many experiments now being carried on. The "stellerator," schematically shown here, is one possible design for a fusion reactor.

We can well imagine the magnitude of the technical task involved in containing a plasma of million-degree nuclei in a confined space, but *if* thermonuclear power can be obtained in spite of great difficulties, it has many inherent advantages over fission power. One is the small amount of radioactivity produced, for there are no radioactive fragments as in the fission chain reaction. In addition, the fuel for fusion—primarily the isotopes of hydrogen—is readily obtained from the sea. There is even a possibility that electrical energy could be withdrawn directly from the plasma, without the intermediate stages of heat energy, then steam, then electrical turbines, which are needed in present electric power plants based on fission.

The magnitude of the job that lies ahead in fusion is well shown by the fact that even now, in spite of diligent efforts throughout the world for several years, it has not been shown conclusively that the thermonuclear reaction has even been attained. Many experiments have been performed with hot plasmas, but the temperatures reached, although difficult to measure, are below a million degrees as yet, hence are far from those really needed for a potent thermonuclear reaction. When it is definitely attained, there still will remain a giant step to the building of a true thermonuclear reactor, one which would generate more energy than is fed into it to maintain the magnetic fields. And we have not mentioned costs. A final step must be taken to produce electrical power cheaper than that obtained now from coal, water power, or the fission chain reaction. A reasonable estimate on the basis of present knowledge is that this last step can hardly be made before the present century ends, if indeed fusion power ever can be economical. In any event, atomic power from fission should not be neglected because of possible competition from fusion in the next few years.

Conclusion

Now we come to the end of our book, but certainly not to the end of the story of the neutron. Already its accomplishments are so varied and so many that we have had to omit some and touch but lightly on others. To the professional physicist we have taken an elementary view of the neutron, but the absence of mathematical complexities by no means robs our story of value. We have seen what immense contributions the neutron has made, and will continue to make, to industrial and engineering progress and to human welfare. We have followed the neutron through the atom's electron cloud into the very nucleus of matter itself. We have learned to appreciate, if not to master, the astonishingly subtle and sophisticated techniques that today's scientists employ in man's never-ending search for the ultimate truth. We have had another revelation of how infinitely intricate are the relationships of subatomic particles, how wondrous the scheme of the universe as revealed in the world of the very small. Since the Greek philosopher Democritus (460 B.C.) applied the word "atom" to the final particle into which matter could be divided, it has been a concept that has enthralled the minds of thinking men. Today we are far, far within so crude an "atom" as Democritus conceived, but the ultimate still eludes us. On some distant day man may stumble upon this ultimate and be able to write the definitive account of matter. If he ever does, the story of the neutron will be one of the great chapters.

SUGGESTED READINGS

Although neutron physics is found primarily in highly technical journals as yet, some parts of our brief neutron story may be pursued further in these books, largely non-technical.

Atoms in the Family, Laura Fermi (University of Chicago Press, 1954). Contains a vivid description of the non-scientific aspects of Fermi's pioneering experiments with neutrons and the building of the first nuclear chain reaction.

Elementary Wave Mechanics, W. Heitler (Oxford University Press, 2nd edition, 1956). The first chapter treats the wave-particle aspects of matter and radiation clearly and with minimum mathematics.

One Two Three—Infinity, G. Gamow (Viking Press, 1947). The properties of sub-microscopic particles, so alien to common sense, are entertainingly described in Chapters 5 and 6.

On Nuclear Energy, D. J. Hughes (Harvard University Press, 1957). The principles of fission, the chain reaction, and the manifold peacetime implications described for the layman.

Atomic Power, a *Scientific American* book (Simon and Schuster, 1955). A series of interesting and accurate articles by authorities in the field, reprinted from the *Scientific American.*

INDEX